The First Juniper Tree

By Adam E. Holton

Self-published 2020 by Adam E. Holton
Copyright © Adam E. Holton, 2020
Music Copyright © Hieronymus Peach, 2020
Cover Design Copyright © Roc Domingo Mesón, 2020

ISBN: 978-3-9519673-1-8

Adam E. Holton has the permission to reprint the poetry of A.S.J. Tessimond in accordance with an agreement between the author and Bloodaxe Books (www.bloodaxebooks.com).

This is a work of narrative philosophy and combines elements of real life and fiction. Permission to use real names has been granted where possible. Any resemblance to actual persons, living or dead, events or places where permission was not possible have been changed to respect the livelihoods and autonomy of those people.

Printed and bound by Tiskárna PROTISK s.r.o. Czech Republic.
Tiskárna PROTISK s.r.o. Rudolfovská 617, České Budějovice 370 01
Tel.: 386 360 136 www.protiskcb.cz

Contact for author: Adam E. Holton   – thoughts@thefirstjunipertree.com

Contact for composer: Hieronymus Peach – hieronymus.peach@gmail.com

www.thefirstjunipertree.com

Thanks to my family for life.

Thanks to E. for love.

Thanks to Dev for his help and patience.

Thanks to Stone for introducing me to Peach.

Note from the author.

Part the way up a mountain,
wedged between Deutschland
and Italia.
Tense and tired, cold hands;
warm heart.
(Visiting Croatia by Alabaster
Deplume)
Friday 13th November 2020
13:09 CET

Dear Reader,

I hope this message finds you well, wherever
and whenever you are. Before you read *The First Juniper Tree*,
I ask for a moment of your time; to clarify one or two elements
of this story.

On the topic of historical accuracy. Some of the
descriptions of Newcastle upon Tyne are from April 2017.
The day on which the conversation between Thomas and
Peach takes place, in my mind, is the 27th April 2018.

I want to make this clear because the dismantling of
the former Odeon cinema on Pilgrim St. and the New Bridge
Project building on New Bridge St. West is described; as well
as the relocation and renovation of Alphabetti Theatre that
took place over the summer of 2017.

On the topic of context. During the three years I have been working on this book, many philosophical, political and economic shifts have occurred.

The ideas that Peach and Thomas explore and discuss in this book were of their own intuiting, during the winter of 2016/2017. There are points of crossover to be found with ideas that are now in the world, that I have discovered towards the end of the writing process.

I believe this coincidence is connected to the individual human ability to divine ideas and thoughts that are present, and shared between all people, in a way that is inexplicable in scientific terms.

Such experiences give me hope.

If you have any questions or thoughts to add about the subject of cultural perspective discussed in this book, then please get in contact with either myself or Peach.

Sincerely,

Adam E. Holton

thoughts@thefirstjunipertree.com
hieronymus.peach@gmail.com

"We are capable of so much more than this."

"But, where do we start?"

"With the simplest and most interesting thing that binds each of us to one another; that we all have to share."

"Our stories?"

"Yes, we start with the stories."

In conversation with Hieronymus Peach

Chapter 1. A doorstep. A departure. A digression.

It was cold outside, but not as cold as it had been.

The west end of Newcastle-Upon-Tyne was dressed in the colours of twilight; just before dawn. The branches of the Rowan trees and Cherry Blossoms stirred a little in the dusty ash-blue light; a pair of magpies already awake and flirting among them. Over the bog of Town Moor, a low mist turned first Dutch pink, then mandarin as the world rolled around; a crescent moon, almost translucent, rested above the supine breasts at the Spital Tongues end. The Ouseburn cascaded through Jesmond Dene in a grey daubed darkness. Armstrong Park, beyond the valley, with oak trees full of superstitious shoes tied to one another. The rouge bricks of the university and the seahorses atop the civic centre bell tower reared up out of the distending shadows. The slow, oily canvas of the Tyne moved under the seven bridges on its passage to the North Sea; glass bottles bobbing along beside the swells. The thrush and hum of traffic began to wash over the city, but the ambulances kept their sirens stilled as they drove closer to the Great North Children's Wing. The mustard and sandstone architecture of Grainger Town was washed with the cool radiance of the sun.

The full length of Grey's Monument was illuminated and the presiding statue of Charles Earl Grey emerged, shit stained and weather worn. The city shrugged and coughed; morning had come on the far edge of winter.

On Sidney Grove a door opened, the lock caught and it was pulled to. Thomas Oliver – pale skinned, sluggish and thin – looked about the street. His face bore the depressions of exhaustion, but his eyes betrayed the smallest glimmer of a private happiness. He sat on the doorstep and leaned back on the cheap, wooden door; the blistered burgundy paint cracked and fell in flakes on his shoulders.

He breathed in. He breathed out.

Most of the street, especially the bottom half towards Nuns Moor Park, had grown accustomed to him sitting there of a morning or night – dressed in tattered long-johns and a dull pea-green hoody with sheep-fur lining. Here, on the step, he drank his coffee, ate his muesli and smoked incessantly. The medical assistants who parked their cars on the street and worked in the old age and vitality clinic, beside the commonwealth war graves, nodded to him. The Bulgarians who washed cars in Howdon greeted him as they passed, the botany and physics students and folk musicians who lived next door waved. The dog-walking retired women stopped and discussed the back alleys and their partners. And before all of these, he saw the drunks as they wandered about, in search of the illegal brothel; asking him first for cigarettes and then for directions. Never a client, but aware of the community around him. The children of the street showed him the games they made with the local cats – drawing figure eights with dry reeds in front of their paws. A theatre set-designer cycled past most days; the young comedians came and shared curry or eggs; the neighbours asked for their parcels. Barefoot and ever the host, sober and welcoming; in spite of his work weary soul.

This morning, as usual, his coffee was well sweetened. He pulled out and un-peeled a satsuma. The door opened and closed behind him. To the doorstep came his friend, Hieronymus Peach.

Peach did not so much sit down, but rather fell onto the perch.

He was still wearing last night's, last month's; last year's suit, beneath a dirty-green Loden great coat, and carried the smell of frankincense, citrus fruit and fag-ash with him. From his suit breast pocket, he pulled a tincture bottle of eucalyptus oil and sniffed a full draught up each nostril. There was a moment of still repose as somewhere inside began the shift of mucus and phlegm that boiled up to the surface. He coughed and snorted gobs of it until it was fresh out of his system and pooled on the pavement before them. Peach, crude and peculiar to some, but his charms and native behaviours were well known to his friend.

"Fetch yourself a cup, Peach, if you want some coffee," Thomas nudged the cafetiere with his bare toes, leaving a smudge on the glass.

Peach did not move to stand. Instead he shifted to his right and leant on his friend. He dropped his hand into a pocket and from it fished a once-white, but not well washed small cup; a gift from his sister, the small silhouette of a juggler beneath the stains.

"I arrive prepared," he held it out in front of his friend with a fiendish grin.

"Give us a cigarette, please." His eyes widened as the coffee was poured. "Ah, better save that one." He coughed again and with his free hand reached up and plucked at the brim of his emerald felt trilby. He found a rather bent, hand-rolled cigarette and put it to his lips. His friend lit it for him and they both leant back on the door.

"Today, Peach. I think I'll go without."

"Do you want me to hold your baccy?"

"Nah, haven't got any left anyways."

Across the street the magpies preened themselves on the branches, showering white petals from the Cherry Blossom onto the pavement. Up to their right a window opened and there was a shout in Arabic, accompanied by house doors, then car doors opened and closed. A taxi drove past, the driver waved at Thomas before turning towards the city, down Studley terrace.

The auroral light made the sky into a pastel palette above them and the din of traffic grew a little louder. The first city bus pulled up across the junction and waited for passengers.

These two young men had known each other for the best part of three decades. Both were born in Derby General on the same February night, but to separate mothers. Peach, the result of a teenage pregnancy, was put up for adoption; whereas his friend was brought up in a stable, but somewhat strange family. They met properly at primary school, each finding their own ways into the same classroom. Apart from a couple years in their early twenties, they moved around the island as if together – guided by coincidence: a village outside of Nottingham, an estate in Slough where Peach's friend almost drowned, another village near the Marlborough Downs in Wiltshire, the gummy streets of Coventry in the West Midlands and now they were living in the same room in the North East.

Peach was the rather more flamboyant and outspoken of the pair. He renamed himself, once of age, under the influence of two peculiar convictions: that like the paintings of Hieronymus Bosch he would look at the whole world, in all of its obscure postures, never shying away from the darkness; until he understood it. And the second was the knowledge that there was always a sweetness in the world, in spite of all the madness and rot. Peach was also the only nickname that ever stuck.

Thomas however, was more solitary and less conspicuous.

Peach in his green boots, violet velvet – paisley patterned – suit jacket and patched black trousers. Thomas, when not at work or lounging about, wore an old, ink blue linen suit from his great-grandfather and pair of suede shoes. The same end of the spectrum, but seen in two different lights.

–

Further to the east, the fishing trawlers returned to the North Shields Fish Quay with their catch. The chandlers' office windows glowed lemon-white as down below generations of men shivered side by side as they unloaded and repacked. Queues of humans, old and everything else, lined the streets of Grainger Town and the outer suburbs for morning buses – in headphone silence or with the April wind in their ears. Large swathes of the city were transformed into silent disco dance floors as the iron hands shifted about clock faces; sweeping them to work or home again from the night shift or to loaf in the city. Forsaken lovers quit affairs on the banks of the river, beneath the Free Trade Inn. Someone cycled across the Tyne Bridge to Gateshead, weaving past a young man staring at the chimneys and cobbles below in the Side. A mother in Heaton cried as her son shat on the staircase after tearing down the door of the toilet. A crusty punk in Sandyford sat alone on his sofa, he complained to the room about his age; his hand resting where his dog once slept. On the corner of Shields and Heaton Road someone still under the influence of ecstasy screamed into a telephone for a taxi. A car careened into the meridian rail on the central motorway near Jesmond, but it didn't roll over the barrier. A pair of relative strangers counted the moments before a shop behind the Byker Wall opened, eager to buy cheap wine to slow down the cocaine. Two friends sat side by side sipping bitter, granulated coffee from tin mugs; trying not to burn their lips. Their thoughts and eyes on the seven and half tons of plasterboard and timber they had only sixteen hands to help carry inside. A bartender in Wallsend lay beside her sleeping friend; crying her regret silently as he snored. A circus Madame in Gosforth stared at an old cash register that stood on her living room table. The back alleys, jewelled with shattered glass and broken televisions, torn mattresses; school-less teenagers; headless trained vines; the reek of grease and chicken bones. In the shadows of St. James' stadium, a man pulled a knife on his friend; not to attack him, just to shut him up. A father in Fenham stirred beside his son inside a red-and-white striped tent in their back garden. A drunkard hammered on the piano in central station. The young women with semi-permanent faces drifted past to their trains; hearing, but not hearing. Noses on High Bridge noted and flinched at last night's piss-wash on the brickwork. The banners of the Theatre Royal billowed and shivered above the people passing by. The debris from last night was cleaned out by the wind, but the acrid smell lingered.

By night, for most of the week, the city was host to the human zoo; all chemical and alchemy mixed with seduction, sedition and Geordie charm. By the end of the second decade of the 21st Century, parts of the city centre will have changed face or shape; vacant spaces and the ruptured skeletons of half-demolished buildings that leered over the streets will have been replaced.

It took a conservative effort to deny them industry, a labour of miseducation to teach them hate, anxiety and cynicism and another decade of dire coalition rule to shake its heart. But beneath it all, the Geordie's are a passionate, honest and tender people.

–

"What do you want to do today, sunshine?" asked Peach.

Thomas sat silent for a moment. He brushed the pool of his palm with his thumb. He stirred for a moment but could muster no salient energy.

"Peach, I'm tired. Today I've woken up early. And for one morning at least, I want to just sit here and wait, watch the street move, maybe eat a little, but just sit here and wait to see what happens."

Peach pulled another satsuma from a pocket inside his jacket and offered it to his friend; one of the many habits shared between them from a young age.

–

On Northumberland Street, a florist was setting up her stall for the day. Always on the same pitch every day – except for Mondays – in between one vibrant department store with green-planted walls and a derelict department store; the notice of departure twisted listlessly on the inside of the glass doors. People walked past it, without looking into the shadows, their eyes trained on the lights of the other shops that seemed brighter now.

She brushed the scented ash blue leaves with her fingers, standing the stems of eucalyptus out in a bucket; next to bunches of gypsophila and Scottish thistles, troughs of potted fuchsia and lazy-headed daffodils, rouge and orange petal tulips beneath the hanging baskets. Her husband handed her an Aloe Vera plant from the back of their van as he closed the door. He softly kissed her lips and knuckles before driving the van away to another job. Standing for a moment, she closed her eyes, steeling herself for the whole day under the gaze of the city. She breathed out, turned the light on under her canopy and began dreaming of selling enough flowers to buy a cabin to keep her warm and sheltered.

–

A young man set out on Sidney Grove, a couple of houses uphill from the pair's stoop, with his coal black Staffy. The dog sniffed and ducked behind the red tongues of crocosmia and poppy heads in search of cats.

Thomas rubbed the arches of his bare feet. He stretched his legs out, flexing his toes.

"How did you sleep Peach?"

"Fine, apart from the slugs. One tried to crawl in my mouth."

"Not hard when you've got a mouth like an eclipse and dreams of felling trees."

"What?"

"You snore, mate, loudly."

"Yeah and you've got a slug problem because the landlord won't fix your wall to meet the floor."

"At least I've got a room."

"I've got one too. I've got yours."

"Then you've got a slug problem too."

Peach elbowed his friend in the ribs, in jest.

"Is there any coffee left?"

"There is always coffee, Peach, help yourself."

Peach poured more coffee for both of them. A slow trail of amber liquid trickled down the side of the awning above them.

"Does your house leak as well?"

"No, it's the Latvian upstairs. He's always drunk and pours the remains of the night before out the window. I've asked him, twice, to stop, but now he just hides from me in the house. Why he can't just pour it down the sink I don't know; shame perhaps?"

Sick of getting splashed, Peach stood and turned his face up to the roof.

"Oi!" Peach roared, "Quit pissing in my coffee!"

Up above there was a clatter of cans and a dull thud; then a window shut.

"Drunks, a sorry and odd bunch of addicts really."

"There was one in that job, she made my life a nightmare."

"At least you're out of there now."

25

Unlike Peach, an odd-jobs man who was invariably skint and more akin with the cats than most other people, Thomas had worked since he was at state secondary school, before the influence of American sitcoms renamed them high schools. Over the years, Thomas had held many jobs, but never settled: site cleaner in a school, manager of a failing pub, head waiter of an Italian restaurant, deckhand in a boat yard on the Avon; he had packed boxes in warehouses for a parcel company; tried working in a green grocers unloading the vans – but was let go for not being nimble enough between the crates in the cellar store room -; he had also harvested fruit until his mind was swollen with chemical fertiliser. All the while, his family and friends had encouraged him towards care work. But it wasn't until loneliness, circumstance and a phone call with a friend that finally found himself in a care role.

For the last two years he had worked as a residential care assistant for the elderly. Most residents had different physical abilities – some in wheelchairs, some non-verbal; some bed bound. And some with severe autism or Alzheimer's. But, even there, he had had trouble fitting in.

The residents liked him well enough, but not the staff. He shared none of their interests in television, diet plans or the vacuum of self-absorbed derision towards other staff in gossip. He was ignored or cut down by some of his colleagues. The few with whom he got on told him he should be somewhere else. He had found humour in the irony of their petty, vicious talk in the role of caring. Not long after it became disgust; one that later became intolerable and forced him to quit.

"She was in her fifties and had been moved around the different floors of the house so much she acted like she ran the place. Bitter and blunt. We drove some of the residents for a trip to Blackpool once and as I sat in the back of the minibus, she decided it was time to tell me why she didn't like me and then tried to excuse herself by saying she was crude and old and not going to change for anyone."

"What did you say to her to start that off?"

"I don't know Peach. I was just sat there."

"Set in her ways much?"

"With the laurel wreath askew. And another time, she tried to get me fired. The other seniors told me she was going to the managers in the morning to accuse me of having a shower on shift, neglecting my responsibilities. I was livid, and that was around the same time one of the resident's sisters, that selfish tyrant, was accusing me of depriving her older brother of his liberty."

"How?"

"On one occasion we were at the pub, out by the coast; one of his favourites. His niece was there and had kept giving him more and more of the dessert that they served in wine glasses. This guy is non-verbal and isn't so self-aware, according to his Dolls assessment. He bit down on the glass and I, fool that I am because he's got a history of biting off peoples' fingers, held his jaw and pulled the shards out. I'm not sitting still if someone's got glass in his mouth. Besides I'm the trained first aider; it's my responsibility. If I didn't do something, I was worried I'd get done for negligence. Then his niece reported me to his sister for grabbing his hand in the Ouseburn when I stopped him from putting firethorn berries in his mouth. And when I told the managers I wanted to raise the case that, from evidence, his sister didn't have the capacity to care for him, which is one of the responsibilities of the job, I got nothing in response, no support."

"Why do you think she couldn't care for him?" Asked Peach.

"I picked him up, after a night at the family flat in Whitley Bay. She pushed him out the door in his wheelchair without a coat, without his trousers fastened, without his foot straps on properly, hefting a bag of winter clothes into my arms and told me he'd eaten four plates of roast dinner and near on a whole treacle cake and closed the door on us, and this had happened to other staff and sometimes worse over the years, but the managers said there was nothing to be done. She was known to be a tough case and what it came down to is the house received a quarter of a million pounds for his care package."

"Fuck. I remember," shouted Peach, "that was around the same time I got fired from the magazine for closing my eyes to listen to the band I was reviewing. I'd been warned about the promoter being a bit of an eel and a coke head. That night he took a disliking to me as I walked down the stairs, coke-venom in his eyes, a grim thing to see, but as I sat down with my eyes closed to listen, shaping the words and sentences for the article, he grabbed me by the throat and pinned me to a wall. The idiot started screaming while the band was still playing and everyone looked. A musician friend of mine left in tears because she was so angry at him. I played it calm, thinking of the magazines' reputation instead of retaliating, but he got to my editor before I did. Lesson learnt, get in first, but shit, how just closing my eyes to appreciate the music got me fired!"

"Fuck, that's what she was."

"Who? What?"

"The guys sister was an editor, of a little boutique magazine for, for, fucking dogs I think."

"For fucking dogs? That's a bit dark."

"No mate, just, the magazine was about dogs, handbag rat dogs on social media." Thomas pushed out his hands and shrugged at Peach, his lips pulled into an appeal. "She would use these words, words like copacetic." Thomas shivered.

"Copa-what?"

"It's OK."

"What's OK?"

"Copacetic."

"Fuck off, it means OK? What a shit!" Peach belched smoke, coughing as he laughed.

"Yeah and on top of her giving me grief, that bitter old drunk, this woman, after the incident with the shower, said she was leaving at the next team meeting. For the whole of her notice period, she kept digging and digging at me, then crying to the managers about fear of moving on, then came out with the funniest thing I had seen in a year when I stopped laughing."

"What?" Asked Peach.

"She attempted reconciliation, redemption perhaps, on our last shift together. The day before she had gone off in a strop, said I'd spoken to her like a child because she flew off the handle at having to stay inside all day with one of the residents who was kicking off, when I'd been out with the same guy I mentioned, about the glass. When we got back from the day out in the city, - man those fourteen-hour shifts were long some days! -, she stood up and strode over to me with something between a leer and an attempt at a smile on her face. In front of everyone, she told me she had left a spare cheese and onion pasty that she didn't want in the oven for me, one of those greasy messes she ate so often. Peach, in that moment I forgot how sad I felt, how shit the past year had been and I just laughed, pealed out in hysterics and walked off to assist this man on the toilet," Thomas wiped the spittle from his lips, "a crap pasty! An unwanted crap pasty! To make up for over a years' worth of vitriol and bullying? It's so pathetic, I couldn't help myself; I think I started crying with laughter. How such a person is allowed to remain working in care is beyond me."

"There's a hard life that makes someone like that, mate." Peach paused and held his friends' forearm. He caught Thomas's gaze and they breathed for a minute, steadying each other's nerves.

Over their heads a starling began its morning call and a street tabby cat roamed about the cars nearby. "At least you got out of there. I think you were right to hand in your notice, then go off sick. I'd have left much earlier than you, not such a patient fuse. How did it go at the doctors the yesterday getting the note?"

"I saw the staff nurse, -the only appointment I could get was seeing the nurse before the surgery was properly open-, at seven in the morning. I didn't tell him I'd already handed in my notice, but just that I couldn't go back. When he asked me why, I started to think of all the things that had happened and broke down. Peach, I wept. Well, started to anyway. Two young men, staring at each other in a doctors' surgery, one in tears and the other at the start of his working day. He didn't have time to listen or let me get it all out. Instead, he agreed to get the doctor to sign a sick note, something about a red flag and handed me the number for Newcastle talking therapy.

"As I stepped outside, I considered calling the help line," Thomas continued, "but I'd called them before. Over six months I'd waited for a response, but none came. These call lines cannot make up for the lack of psychological support on this island and, if the Tories keep it up, they'll probably just cut the staff and install an answer machine. I folded up the card, put it back in the surgery post box. I just needed relief from the bullying and having to put on a face. I know I'm soft in some ways Peach, but what's the point in having to toughen up for them? That means they've won, that my free will is co-opted by their disgusting behaviour, that I have to change, not them. It's crooked, but it's over."

"At least you're out of the acid bath now, sunshine."

"True. But there were some moments that were not so shit. There was another senior who could always listen. She told me about her guardian angels and I would have loved to hear more of her stories. One of the night shift ladies, this incredible, kind Polish lady, she was great. And there was another guy who came from down stairs. He was funny. We were out driving with a resident one day and he told me I wasn't a tree. 'Yea, there are two types of people' he said. 'There are trees and there are people who are not trees. The trees stay, always, but the others move out like the wind'."

Thomas leant back on the door frame. The freshness of the morning air bristled his cheeks and teased the blood to the surface. He looked up at the branches of the Rowen tree across the street; slowly coming into life after winter's death.

"Do you want a laugh?"

"Sure," replied Peach, making fists and releasing them.

"After I got back from the doctors yesterday – I think you must have slept through this – but I hadn't so much as closed the front door before a rapping knock came. I opened it to face a woman, dressed all in black, waving a sheet of paper at me."

"Jehovah's witness?"

"Ha! not quite. Bloody bailiff, from a private company representing the courts, with a warrant to cut off the gas and electric. Turns out the landlord owes the utilities company over three thousand. He didn't even turn up in court. He gets the money for the gas, electric, water and council tax out of the rent I pay. When I managed to get him on the phone after having to repeatedly send him messages - arsehole only responds when it's anything to do with money -, I handed him over, well the phone, over to the bailiff. She put him on loud speaker because she was also on the phone to her boss. I had refused to let her and the engineer enter the house because it wasn't my responsibility and I'm not having the utilities shut off because of a dick of a landlord. He started going on about the account being put in someone else's name, one of those door knocking scams. He blamed it on a previous tenant who had signed up. After about half an hour of this, and over hearing that he owns over fifty properties in the city, the bailiff left. When I called him back to ask if he wanted a photo of the warrant letter I'd been given I learnt whose name the account was in, guess who?"

"Who's?"

"His mother's! Turns out he has accounts under his name, his brothers' and his mothers' name. And he doesn't give us due notice when people are turning up to clean or do repair work. He lives over in Liverpool. The old joke in the house was that, really, he lives on a yacht in Malta. Only talks to you when you mention money and the contract's a fix. He's not liable if he breaks contract, but the tenants are. I needed somewhere to live and it's all I could afford, but hospitable landlord my arse. There's seven of us in here, used to be eleven with the couples sharing rooms, the kitchen's half broken, gets flooded if you flush the downstairs toilet too often, the fridge is perma-broke, the upstairs shower trips the fuses most days and the wall in my room doesn't meet the floor."

"And the slugs," Peach joined in.

"And the bloody slugs."

"So why don't you move?"

"Because I can't afford to and I like this street. I just have to think of Chekhov the playwright and it gets a little easier."

"You still do that?"

"Too right, it's bloody everywhere: Chekhov or Stephens. They get the mess of this life on the daily level and to whisper either of those names helps when it feels like I'm entering that absurd world again. And the scary thing is, that so little has changed! I used to have to do it when I sat around the dinner table with the staff at that old place. Chekhov would have loved it, a dinner table, everyone talking and no one listening apart from one in the corner who hears it all and swims beneath the ice."

"We've all got our tricks I suppose. Odd how, even after decades, their stories still fit. Want some more coffee?"

"Please Peach."

"Does the kettle still work?"

"I hope so."

Peach pulled himself up, using the wall and Thomas' shoulder. He went back inside, leaving the door ajar. He stuck the kettle onto boil, then went into the bedroom they shared beside the front door.

Thomas sat watching the pair of magpies across the street. He thought of his father and the nursery rhyme he was taught as a child. He heard the sound of Peach playing the electric piano he borrowed from a neighbour. They'd set it up at the bottom of Thomas's bed, in front of the stopped-up fire-place. Peach had his own peculiar style of playing the piano, being self-taught he called it ragtime punk, although sometimes he would play a piece that he called Lilac Iris.

It was soft and sombre, each phrase washing over you; almost hypnotising. In parts it was melancholic, in E and B minor, quite unlike his usual raucous music. He appeared transformed when he played this piece; meditative and serene. For a man who was seldom quiet, it was a moment to behold; the inner sound of a soul he never quite shared with the rest of the species, but one that Thomas knew lay just underneath all the revelry and audacious behaviour. Once you got to know Peach you could understand why some of his friends considered him a handful, a tempest; a lovely nightmare.

Most days, - on his lunch break or after work renovating a local theatre -, he went down to the grand vault of the Central station entryway where, in a small glass alcove beside the front doors, stood an old and slightly out of tune upright piano. The high ceilings held his sustained notes or boomed with the echo of him hammering out a descending blues in A or D minor. His hat on the floor beside him for spare change and his ears open to listen to anyone who cared to tell him a story. He learnt to play in time, he said, by listening to the rhythm of peoples' steps as they walked to-and-fro in the room.

The music stopped and a moment later Peach sat down with the coffee. He set about rolling another cigarette. In his deliberations he could become so focused that the whole world and his essence were distilled into a single action. One of the cigarette papers came loose from the packet and was caught in the breeze, suspended before him in the morning air. He plucked it out of the ether, and sat there with it, between thumb and forefinger, his gaze fixed on it. He sighed.

"There is something, a simple satisfaction, in catching paper out of the wind," declared Peach. He turned to his friend with the high cheeked smile that made him look simultaneously childish and manic.

"Yes Peach. That piece you were playing reminds me of a poem, have I ever told you?"

"Which one?"

" *'With a little more time or a little more patience, one might'*"

" *'Disentangle for separate, deliberate, slow delight,"* Peach joined in, *"one of the moment's hundred strands, unfray beginnings from endings, this from that, survey say a square inch of the ground one stands on'* It's Tessimond!"[1]

"Right, and that's how I feel when I listen to it and that's how I feel today. I usually carry a copy of it in my jacket pocket. It's odd the things people carry with them."

"Have you ever read any poetry from Carver?"

"Don't think so, who's Carver?"

"Carver was an American author. He wrote a poem called *At Least* which always puts me in a reflective mood. He sets about describing the world he is accustomed to and, in naming it, evokes a sense of awe. Not nostalgia. A kind of active

---

[1] A S J Tessimond, *Collected Poems* (Bloodaxe Books, 2010) www.bloodaxebooks.com

reflection. Just watching the world go by, making his own conclusions. Simple, decisive, genius. There is no malice in this desire to reach conclusions. They have no greater impact on the reader or the world, they are Carver's alone. And in that, I find," said Peach prodding his chest with his forefinger, "the sense of curious play that we are all entitled to. And it really makes me wonder about my own conclusions, that I draw from the world I see. Are they my own? But I digress. It's about patience, to me, and reflection. If I ever became King of England," Peach said, raising his chest and fondling the lapels of his jacket, "I'd ask people to read those two poems and I'd play Lilac Iris for them. Just for due consideration."

They shuffled on the step to warm their arses. Tufts of the peeling paint stuck to Peach's coat and Thomas brushed some from his hair.

"Want to hear a funny story about that piece of music, mate?"

"Go for it Peach and cheers for listening to my rant."

"You're welcome," he lent into Thomas, pushing his friend playfully. "So," he continued, "I once played that piece of music in a high Catholic church in Leamington Spa."

"What were you doing in a church?"

"Practicing piano. I might not be a devotee, in a theistic sense, but churches are interesting places, to me, the architecture designed to amplify sound, the history of the places, the myth and folklore behind each column, the curious congregation that gathers, or doesn't gather, but I always find something in them, or something or someone finds me in them. They also, in my experience, usually have a piano."

"What do you mean – finds you in them?"

"That morning I was waiting for a train out of the West Midlands, I had a little time to spare and I remembered a midnight mass my mother had taken us to where I ended up hugging the bishop in all his giant gowns because he'd got suspicious when I hugged the choir girls as they passed, coming back in when you give everyone your blessings."

"Peach."

"I know, but the gesture in my mind was innocent, anyway, I remembered seeing a piano that night and so I went back to see if it was still there and to ask if they wouldn't mind my

42

practicing whilst I waited for the train. I was all clean coat and hands clasped behind my back to the church master and she obliged my request; she even helped me move the old Kimball baby grand into the heart of the transept. I sat and played, watching a group of older women preparing some flower decorations in the nave. There weren't many others in the church that morning, but one woman, a visitor, came up and thanked me. I turned to her and explained Lilac Iris is a piece about reflection. She said she knew what I meant, she nodded and her eyes welled up a little. Then she told me she had sat, listening, and had thought of her husband who had died five weeks ago and had felt a little calmer, if only for a moment. I stood and spread my arms out and she embraced me and we stayed like that for some time, her crying on my chest. I held her until I could feel her grip loosen and I opened my arms. I smiled a little when she called me an angel. When she stepped away there was a man stood behind her shadow. He cocked his head and said he was here to practice the organ. He asked if I would like to see how it works. Curious, I sat beside him as he played Bach with his feet on this grand machine.

"As he described how the stops and pedals worked, we got to talking about when he had learnt to play. As a child he'd been adopted as well and, at five, his mother, adamant he was to have a respectable future, sent him for piano lessons. Years later, when he was about fifteen, he sang in the men and boys' choir in a small village near Bakewell. After practice he'd huddle round the organ playing with the other boys to listen to the power of the thing. The organist, it turned out, knew about the boy and his ability with the piano and one day told him he should learn the organ. He wouldn't teach him as such, but would advise him. All this was not too long after the Second World War. A month or so later, the vicar came and asked the young man to play the organ for the sermon."

"What about the organist?"

"The organist was indisposed, convalescing. The petrol tank on the motorbike he rode around on had caught fire and burnt his arse so he couldn't sit down.

"Ha brilliant! Well not really, but brilliant."

"His name was Michael, the guy in the church. The day I met him he was in his mid- seventies, retired and relieved after a life in mathematics. He did excuse himself though."

"What for?"

"'Excuse me' he said 'I hope you don't mind, but I'm not really a religious man, I just come here to practice the organ.'"

"Two atheists sat at the altar."

"All for the love of music. But it reminds me of Paris."

Thomas gathered the frayed, open halves of his hoody and pulled them in to his chest. He lifted his heels up and drew them to the doorstep. He clenched and unclenched his fists. Peach was a tangential sort of storyteller. He would often connect points of his own life in a way that made sense to him, but not always to others. One could imagine the necessity for a witness to be present in his life, at all times; in order to later relay the foundation for certain leaps or connections. Though possible, Peach hadn't found one; nor was he about to record everything through social media. There was enough of that about. Perhaps all it required was Peach to give a bit more context and slow down before he introduced the next episode. Or, perhaps it was the intimate art of listening that had changed.

"What's the connection to Paris?"

"That interesting things happen to me in the houses of the holy. The moment that came back to me was what happened in the bowels of the Sacre Coeur."

"When were you in Paris?"

"Years ago, the spring after the world was supposed to end, remember?"

"Ah, yeah. Twenty twelve. So, what happened in Paris?"

"I was there with an ex-partner, the one who I found the piano for. The piano my 56-year-old dad and two friends helped me carry up six flights of stairs on Charlotte Street to the attic flat I once lived in. That was a hard morning. My dad at the bottom end with a mate who's now in the army engineers. We almost dropped it on the fourth corner, shit, we left a hole or two in that stairwell wall. All of that sweat and swearing for the same ex-partner who said she played the piano, but then never did. That's when I learnt to do something active instead of getting angry and taught myself to play. But I digress.

"We were in Paris for a few days on the way to Madrid by train because she was afraid of flying and I'd been curious about the Sacre Coeur so we went in, after getting trapped for a while in the once dishevelled haunt, now tourist trap, of Montmartre. My French was not great so she translated the sermon for me that we walked in on. Sat in the back row, with her whispering in my ear, I looked out over the whole congregation. The priest, in all his fangled finery, told of two types of people who exist in the world today. Keep in mind; please," Peach started jabbing the sky with his finger, "this was before the American redefinition of the word 'wall'. 'There are the people who will arrive somewhere' the priest said 'and help to build the walls of community and there are those,' and here he spread out his cloaked arms in a gesture to encompass the whole cathedral and the flow of tourists ambling about in the side of the nave, where they were flashing cameras and squawking all the while, 'those who will arrive and want no part in the building of a wall or house or sacred place, but will be satisfied to stand by and be photographed beside one, but that satisfaction will be hollow'.

"Now, remember, this isn't about American 'walls', the ones that shut people out. But the walls that can house a community! And I agreed with that idea; still do. Not being

47

religious it seemed to resonate more strongly within me for some reason. I'll never forget the sense of sober clarity that I felt. Even the houses of the holy are concerned about the trepidation of our species to work together for something," Peach poked the air beside Thomas, "note how he said sacred *places* and not churches or cathedrals. There must be something in that. He was talking beyond the cloth of his belief and about humans, about all of us."

Peach lowered his hands down, warming them behind his knees as he tucked his legs up.

"But this sermon stuck and came back to my mind the last time I was here."

"When?"

"You don't remember? Last summer."

"Ah, yeah, because you were helping to build that theatre."

"Right, and the three months building it were a peculiar time, but the voice of the priest came to me again on the opening night. I sat in the back row of the rake after Ali's speech and wondered where all these people had been during the build. I had recognised a few of them, and indeed some must have been there when I hadn't, but most of them I had never seen. There was the odd face I knew from when the theatre was in the basement of New Bridge Project, but they hadn't helped build. I just sat and watched. They came, they drank, and they discussed themselves with one another on the low-lit stage."

"Perhaps, they didn't know how to build or were busy?"

"I accept that, but when I arrived, I didn't know how to build a wall, I learnt on the job hanging through the gas pipes and standing on thin air in the wall cavities to hammer in the insulation. 'Is it to do with anxiety?' I wondered. 'Do some people worry about engaging with a task they don't already understand, for fear of being seen as incapable?' The theatre would post messages on social media sites asking for help and you could see how many people had looked at the message, but the responses always came from the same few, not to mention the let downs and the loss of skilled labourers from the college. It had to be done because there has to be, in my opinion, a theatre like that in the city, but it's difficult to contend with the idea that it is the few, at present, who take on the work of so many; it is a shared responsibility, no?"

"Enough! Hold on mate. Can you at least slow down? I can't wrap my brain around that kind of question now. Do you know what time it is?"

"Yes."

"Well fine for you. Can we go for a walk or something?"

"Fine by me."

Thomas stood up to get a pair of shoes and a bigger jacket.

Chapter 2.   To Town Moor and the past.

The bus stop at the bottom of Sidney Grove had changed
shape. The rolled shoulders of care workers, the arthritic
coroners with blistered knuckles, the taut cheeks of the nurses,
the grimace of a delayed baker had all arrived elsewhere. Now
the slouch of students, the shuffle of bank tellers and the
breakfast lullaby shift bartenders perched under the awning and
lent on the fences. Peach's scarf hung from the left trick pocket
of his Loden coat. Thomas put his hands up to the sun as they
turned onto Brighton Grove. The garden of the clock tower
house was scorched in places, from the burnt-out aerosol cans
tossed by teenagers. Plastic bags swam about their calves as the
taxis and school runs filled the road. They passed the derelict
plot on Nuns Moor park, where allotments had flourished
before they were ruined by hired vandals and the freeman of
Newcastle reclaimed the plot on account of negligent tenants.
Torn down, the earth chewed up by claw hand industrial
tractors and then abandoned after a planning permission
oversight led to the collapse of a building contract.

They sprinted across the junction, through the backed-up
traffic outside BBC Newcastle. Past the blood-bank and the
body shop behind it. The grubby scruffs of grass and earth

51

teased apart the paving slabs on Hunters road. The houses all wore 'to let' signs that had never been taken down, all hangover quiet and dormant. The railings by the corner shop, hunched over from when a VW Passat lost a street race. The gardens of the council houses were in need of more nurturing. An elderly woman waved at them from her living room as they passed by.

They crossed over Claremont and walked up onto the bridge above the city motorway. Without a word they both slowed down and, resting their forearms on the barrier, turned their faces toward the city and the sun as the earth continued to roll around.

Unlike Peach, Thomas hadn't settled so well in Newcastle. He had never really explored it. Two and a half years was a while in a city, by any standards, but up until yesterday he'd only seen it whilst working, or hemmed in on a bus or tucked into a carriage of the Metro heading to the coast. He loved the view of Newcastle from above the Byker Bridge, as the buildings appeared once you emerged from Manors station. He always found ways to turn towards it. The city fascinated him and it filled his dreams, but he felt he had no time to become a part of it.

It hadn't been the football, nor the sea; nor was it the university that had brought him North, but an offer of a change from a friend of his.

Thomas had, in his early twenties, met a woman called Mary. By chance, they had been across the street from one another near the Tanners Arms in Leamington Spa. She was standing with a spade in one hand and a coffee cup in the other. He was idling about on a day off. He stopped walking and stared at her. Their eyes met. He crossed over and said she had a nice spade, and asked what was she going to do with it, and would she like any help. She said yes. They walked to her house and buried a dead fox that had appeared in her back garden. When they were finished, she put the kettle on and they carried on talking. She worked for a theatre company, as a seamstress and set designer. Her broad and peculiar curiosity in fabrics and her thin, charming smile aroused him.

As they got to know each other, Thomas learnt that she was always with purpose and usually without time, at the usual times, but somehow always about. Thomas fancied her, but it came to nothing. It welled up inside him, but he lacked a simple kind of assertiveness. He suffered constant harassment from the people he worked with and it came to dampen his self-confidence. Bars and pubs aren't for the thin-skinned. He couldn't muster an interest in their shit chat either. Opinions about clothes, about phones, about a tv series, about the paraphernalia from the 90's rave scene they bought on the internet, about their axles, about their council bills. He was interested in them as people, but could never got beyond the superficial details. He never suited the furore of the inebriated, nor the tension of tending them, but at that time he didn't know what else to do workwise. It tore at his self-esteem and often made him sullen. Then, Mary moved to Newcastle.

Having not heard from her for two years, he called one night whilst out walking along the section of the Grand Canal that ran through the town. As he kicked stones into the black water, the call had connected. They chatted a while as she sewed petals onto a costume in her workspace. She listened as he bemoaned the job and the relentless hollow feeling he had between his throat and his hips. She interrupted his harangue of the customers and said she knew of someone who needed a care assistant for her son. She asked if he would be interested. And there was a spare room in her house until he found somewhere to sleep.

He quit the West Midlands and moved North. Everything he had fitted into a single suitcase and a rucksack. She met him at Central station and they walked home together, up the West road. Thomas took to the care role well enough and it led to more work, but living at Mary's became uncomfortable. It was never clear where the boundaries were. One night they kissed and shared a bed, but nothing more. It never fit together.

Thomas grew confused and more frustrated the longer he had to wait to be paid. He'd arrived with little left over from the previous job. When the pay came, it was only enough to cover rent and a bit of food. The other people in the house were eccentrics and acrobats who kept their own hours; loudly. The nuances of the young men he assisted, the tension between him and Mary and the drawing out of the days when he was skint all sank in. After three months he found a cheap box room in a shared house on Sidney Grove and moved in.

In a bid to earn more and sort himself out, he took on a job as a residential care assistant. But from the first day he had a bad feeling about the residence. There was a weird vibe there, a bitterness that lingered about the place and in the faces of some staff. He knew the sneer and the smell of indifference that came from shit pay and not enough recognition. The consequences of the 14-hour shifts – that began before sunlight – the faults of the hoists and equipment, the need for constant delicacy with the elderly, vulnerable bodies; the diminishing friendship with Mary and not knowing how to get on with the staff sank deeper into him. He began drinking his way through his time when not at work.

The only moments he got to share with Mary where in chance meetings or rushed coffees at the station as she was going elsewhere – his shoulders littered with eczema petals; his gums rotting. Each time she stepped onto the train, or left him in the street, he began to unravel.

–

Peach offered him a slice of satsuma.

"What are you looking at?"

"Just watching the cars come and go," replied Thomas.

"Fancy going to the city later?"

"Perhaps, or the coast. Let's carry on up the Moor. It's loud here."

Peach linked arms with Thomas and turned to the left. He was pushed away, but not too far. They sloped down the path, through the half gate and out onto the Moor. Larger than Hyde Park and Hampstead Heath put together, home to the scream, stench and cacophony of the Hoppings fair in June and the quiet mulling of cattle throughout the year. Pools of light glowed between the folds of the field; trenches riven in other centuries. A young heron took flight. The Moor preacher navigated the border fences – wrapped in a damp, knee length rugby coat padded out with greasy sheep's wool and newspaper – shouting to the sky about starlings and discussing anger with his council of selves. Runners and a drunk teenager filled up the path before them. Beyond the fences, towards Jesmond, the gutted-out Palace of Arts stood wrapped in scaffold. Soon to be a brewery bar; soon to be busier than before.

They turned left off the tarmac and traipsed up the nearest of the hills on the moor. Peach claimed to be convinced they were the breasts of the city, enamoured by the thought that there was a feminine soul rooted and welded into the place. At the summit they turned again towards the South.

"You know what I said before," began Peach.

"No, which bit?"

"Whether the people helped out building the theatre or not."

"I mean there's a lot of reasons for people to not help," interrupted Thomas. "Time, who really has time? And not everyone is as confident as you to just turn up and learn on the job?"

"Why deny oneself the possibility? Ali gave people the opportunity to come and help out and to show them, as best he can, how to build stuff. There's a moment in the imagination that overwhelms us, where we're confronted by the enormity of the challenge upon us. When it feels that you alone have got to go onto to build the whole theatre and rewire the building and save the country's culture scene, and, and. We project that burden onto a single set of shoulders. It's no wonder the prospect of starting such a thing is too scary."

"So why are you pissed off with them for not helping?"

"I'm not pissed off with that, or them. The person not helping is a consequence of being conditioned to not develop the sense of curiosity that allows one to engage with the unknown, because they either can't imagine it or blow it out of proportion. I am not angry with the individuals who didn't come, I'm fucked off with how they've been taught that behaviour."

"So, how are you going to change that, almighty Peach?"

"Mate, don't get snarky with me. I think there is a need to spread the blame proportionately. Then deal with it. If not, then the individual gets left to shoulder it. Creating a more balanced expectation of the self is healthy and learning to build communities or theatres is a shared responsibility that can help that."

"And you get to announce that to everyone?"

"The individual needs to be able to see themselves as part of a situation where that shared responsibility is possible. Besides, when I started building there was Dene and Joe and that pretty Frenchman, Arnaud, who showed me how to plaster. There is guidance everywhere, but stepping into the room is the start."

Peach looked down and pulled his baccy pouch out of a pocket. His fingers and hands were scored with veins of violet and orange. Underneath the nicotine smudges and dirty fingers, the lack of blood flow was uncomfortable to look at; but beautiful in an abstract kind of way and he thought so too. To deal with the nicotine stains, he had got into the habit of carrying a lemon with him everywhere; in one of his many pockets. Throughout the day he would cut into it and scrub the pulp across the brown patches to clean them off his skin.

On the moor below them the streetlights flickered off.

"So, you don't think everyone has to be pushed into it at first?" Asked Thomas.

"No, just willing to have a go. There is no guilt in not knowing how to do the thing you've never done before. And there's no shame in fucking up. So long as no one's on fire, you're usually doing alright."

"You and you're fucking fires Peach."

Thomas jabbed him just above the elbow. Peach dropped the cigarette he was making. Thomas sidestepped Peach's lunge.

"Wasn't me mate. I was possessed you know. That angel of yours was using me again."

"Piss off Tom, I'm cutting back."

"Yeah, yeah and I'm just an angel, pissing on your tabs."

Peach pulled at the folds on his tobacco pouch, fingering the dry threads inside. Then closed it again, shoving it deeper into an inside pocket.

A chain of cyclists made their way across the moor to Jesmond. Thomas watched them for a while. When he'd been working in the residence, he would walk across the moor to and from work. In the mornings it could be bitter cold and sodden underfoot. He once had a bicycle, but it got stolen from outside City Library. Waking up early enough to get to work was a struggle. He often didn't have time to eat. He didn't have the time to let his body get into a position to be able to digest anything. It only got more difficult the more he drank in the evenings. Soon enough, he only drank a rank, granulated coffee with a heap of sugar before he divagated over the moor to his shift.

In a morning, his responsibilities would be, invariably, help the male residents get ready for breakfast and to meet whichever therapist, or consultant was due that day. There was always a race on. The baths that didn't work properly. The disgruntled senior screaming out about the medication cards that "fucking John had fucked up again," always blaming someone else. The preparation. The toileting. The eating. The toileting. The shouting. The screeches of laughter. It was raucous and Thomas even enjoyed it some mornings, but it got harder to keep his misery in check the hungrier he got. He watched as some of the staff would help themselves to food. He had started doing the same, after a couple of weeks of being there, but got pulled aside for it by the manager. He started carrying two eggs and a couple slices of bread in his pockets across the moor to cook and eat after the shift; before heading home again to sleep. Often, he wouldn't know what to do with the time in between shifts. A malaise had set in, curtailing his desire to read or try and meet people. He worried about these things, ignoring the genuine weariness he felt from the job. Care roles are physically demanding and emotionally exhausting. He confused real tiredness with a sense of longing, a sense of dread and a sense of loneliness. It was nauseating, until it was too much.

Peach faked lunging at him. Thomas jumped back.

"Well you're faster than I remember for a miserable bastard."

Peach lunged at him again, this time for real. Thomas slid to his right on the muddy earth and stuck out his foot, catching Peach on the knee. Peach threw his weight into his shoulder and corkscrewed into Thomas. They both fell backwards onto the slope of the moor like cubs in play. The light fell across their eyes and Thomas flashed his teeth. Peach had always found a moment, no matter how deep Thomas sank in the past, to pull this playful nature out of his friend. He gave him space to be silly, a companion in raggedy mess making. In the innocent furore of real play that is the reserve and right of all humans – of all ages – we find our way back to ourselves.

"Another digression, similar tangent, but this example is from Innsbruck," started Peach as he rose to his feet at the bottom of the hill.

"Peach! Enough. Sometimes listening to you is like looking at the future, no matter which way I turn I can't escape it."

Peach fell silent and stuck his hands in his pockets like a sullen child as Thomas stood and scraped off the grimy mud.

"Ok, so how about breakfast at Moulin Rouge to start the day?" Asked Peach.

"Yes, that's an idea and how about out to the Coast later. Alright?"

"Fine. But can I carry on while we walk?"

"Perhaps."

Chapter 3. Breakfast at Moulin Rouge.
Shifting perspectives.

Peach sat in Thomas's room, waiting for him to finish in the shower. He plied the sustain pedal on the keyboard. He muttered his dreams from beneath closed eyes. He longed to pedal a pump organ or the brass feet of a real piano; not just the synthesised breathing of electricity. He rambled on, quiet and occasionally dropping a finger on a key then looking about the room; as if searching for a reaction of some kind.

His makeshift bed was on a sofa they had carried down from the living room on the first floor. The scuffed blue covers were hidden by a frayed, tartan shawl; his paint-spattered, patched up work trousers and his only other blue cotton shirt. There was a notebook by the pillow. His singing bowl on the shoulder.

He watched the book spines on a shelf up to his left as he tapped the keys. Rested on the mantlepiece in front of him was a metre square canvas. Vivid midnight blue paint surrounded the portrait bust of a naked woman whose head was an explosion of admiral butterflies. Thomas's work desk stood before the street level windows, hidden by a gossamer curtain; moving in the breeze.

Peach's chair rested against the edge of Thomas's raised, double mattress. Above the bed was a Tunisian tapestry, sewn gold on a dark blue that mirrored the painting. The image on the fabric was of fish swimming amongst leafy branches around a star encased in a globe. On the floor lay a woven, multicoloured rug. A friend of Thomas's had once hung it in an exhibition, calling it *'A night sky above Glasgow.'*

The morning light filled the room.

Thomas came in. His bare chest raw and mottled from the hot water. Steam rose from his forearms and ribs as he stood in the doorway. He left the towel on the bed and walked to the cabinet beside Peach to look for some clothes.

"Feel better, mate?" He continued testing out the notes on the room.

"I do, but now I'm hungry. Are you ready to go?"

"As soon as that shirt is over your head." Peach stood, pushed Thomas onto the bed and walked out of the room. "I'm heading up Dilston. Catch me up."

Thomas took the Fenham road to cross over to Dilston. He saw the tails of Peach's coat as they disappeared behind the corner house. He ran to catch up. The branches of the trees along the terraced street were littered with fat, young buds and children's toys, hung blankets and crisp packets. Swivel chairs and sofas were already outside some of the front doors. Children pushed siblings and neighbours around on plastic tricycles. A group of teenagers sat discussing their phones in Polish beside the Potraveny Tatry. They crossed over Stanhope street, next to women in violet and turquoise saris pushing prams full of rice sacks. A blacked-out BMW overtook the number 40 bus and missed a capped old man by a foot or two. The shutters drawn on the halal takeaways rattled. Above the din of traffic, shouts could be heard from Hutchinson's' vegetable shop. The burnt sugars and cinnamon from Ayesha's mixed with the diesel fumes, the body sweat; the reek of turmeric and yeast. The knackered sprinter vans, driven by crusty-cheeked men and their uncles beside them, passed this way and that.

Thomas and Peach carried on, past the Wesleyan Methodist church. Upturned sofas wedged in gateways, German

Shepherds in bandanas; the sound of a man warming his voice up in a first-floor window. At Westgate road, a strong smell of a morning joint being passed behind the hedge at Grainger Hotel. Articulated lorries trapped in junctions. Whining mopeds. The shouts of Armenian and Somalian morning song. The greasy white walls of the bowling alley beneath the 'For Sale' sign. The glassless bus shelter in front of The Rose restaurant. The menacing and meek faces in the barbershops, all receiving the same short-back and sides; no matter what they asked for. A mosaic of more languages flew about them as they passed a billboard that displayed "Summer Getaways" with *'like fuck'* scrawled underneath it. Quiet queues waited outside slim-shelved bakeries for the billowing white loafs within. The door on the Lebanese spice shop stood ajar, the scent of cloves and curry masalas floating into the street. The shutters were rolled up on Najeb's market and a light came on in the bookies on the corner. An older man in overalls, bristly face and grey skinned, sold an opened pack of cigarettes to a woman with a baby slung on her hip before he went inside to bet. A slab of meat as big as a bookshelf, abandoned and defrosting, lay on the grassy knoll across from the Westgate Baptist church. A taxi driver, sharp shoulders and a Kenyan grin, listened to a sermon on his mobile phone as he waited outside. Todds Nook, Westgate Court and Vallum Court stood tall and proud, above adverts for obesity campaigns and vape pens, that pictured young, white men atop a mountain, claiming to "take back your freedom" at the bus stop. The war memorial graves were hidden beneath budding sycamores and hawthorn bushes. A drunk woman wolf whistled at a middle-aged couple outside the Krishna centre. The clock on the Hillsong church told the right morning hour and deeper in the city the peal of bells rang out.

They descended onto the lower half of West road, amongst the Turkish and Romanian restaurants, the motorbike mechanics and the hock shops; the dry houses and the wet. First floor tattoo parlours and the pension queue outside the post office door. Then the Moulin Rouge on the corner. The Persian greasy spoon of the West End.

There was a small table free, behind a gang of builders. Peach ordered two veggie halal breakfasts and ushered Thomas into the corner.

The builders were loud and there was a tabloid on the table.

"But, mate, nah like. It's just shite."

"Look. Here mate," the foreman turned his head from one of his bricklayers to the café owner and nodded, almost imperceptibly, before asking him "where are you from?"

"Tehran," he said, turning away from the coffee machine for a moment. He rested his elbow on the register.

The foreman returned to his bricklayer, "so, you, you're telling me you'd believe the shite in there over the fact that this guy here is a welcoming host and has just cooked you a delicious breakfast?"

"Howay, mate, give in."

"Nah, think it through. If you still think he should fuck off, maybe you should make his breakfast for a change. Or what about Terry?"

At the end of the table a younger man raised his head. A pair of warm, olive coloured eyes focused on the foreman. He ran his hand through his short, slovenly hair and smiled; revealing a set of limpid false teeth.

"What about Terry?"

"Exactly! He ain't done nowt but work since he got here. You can make his as well."

"Nah, aye I'll think on it."

Terry imitated him and a couple of them laughed.

"Aye, fucking idea that" was the concluding remark from the foreman and they fell into a different chat, flexing their plaster caked jackets. Another block of flats was going up·nearby. Luxury is what it said on the signage. The cafe owner turned back to his coffee machine with coy smile after his rehearsed exchange.

"How some people define things is a fraud Tom, did you know that?"

"How so Peach? Thanks." The breakfast arrived. Peach got to the brown sauce first.

"This lot are building them flats on the corner. That will go up as a fuck off eyesore in the name of luxury. But is it? Really? It'll go up as fast as possible and who will move in?"

"Don't know."

"Me neither, but it's no wonder there's grief in people who are losing the city centre to the lack of imagination these property developers have. I mean, why is it always fucking flats?"

Thomas pushed the mushrooms and onions around in the beans and brown sauce.

"So, what did you want to say about Innsbruck Peach? Sorry for cutting you off on the Moor."

"Ah, yes. Innsbruck," his wrists rested on the table and he stared at his breakfast, then at the fish tank, then at Thomas before he continued, "after helping out at a festival in Italy last Autumn, living in a ramshackle cabin with the wind and the rain, I was invited to Hall-in-Tirol where I lived in a caravan in a friend's garden. It's just over the border into Austria. One night he took me to an open mic night in Innsbruck, about seven minutes down the train line. During a chat with the organiser, before the music started, I asked if there was any stand-up comedy in the city, or in Austria. I'd been thinking about Lauren, you know, who lives next door to you? Well, turns out there isn't any stand-up comedy, really, in Austria.

So, I thought to do a little experiment. I played a couple of songs at the end of the night and as I stood next to the organiser, I asked the audience, about a hundred fifty or so people, who of them wanted to see stand-up comedy in Innsbruck. The crowd cheered and raised their arms. And in the next breath I asked, who wants to help me? The whole room fell silent. That abject silence I imagine when the loneliness or the insecurity creeps in. I held my breath, still no hands went up. So, I shouted, 'Ok, no comedy for Innsbruck then.' And the room laughed, as if released from the threat of responsibility." He took a swig from his cooled coffee.

"I thought it over and what bothered me was that, perhaps, people are really comfortable being consumers of stuff. They don't know, have forgotten or never learnt how to be part of a process in a meaningful way."

"Or maybe they don't want to be? I mean we are all part of a work process somehow, so where would you get the energy for more?" Asked Thomas.

"That's a thing! It's exhaustion, we don't have time or energy to engage with the things we think or know we want. Even if they may be better for us than what we have now. Perhaps, it's because of the insecurity thing. Perhaps, it's the missed step between consumption and meaningful participation, where people get snagged on the grim, remedial slogan that suggests the best salve is to buy your way into or out of a situation, instead of being a part of creating it."

"It's pretty popular to watch the 'making-of' kind of shows though."

"Yeah, but if such a passive act doesn't lead to genuine participation, I don't think it's healthy; it's not satisfying the person's innate curiosity – it leaves that curiosity in limbo. There are lots of people working on interesting projects in lots of places, so, it's not universal. But there is something that causes some people to just sit and watch, or wait for someone else to do it. That's the bit that worries me."

"But what is it?"

"I reckon, it's caused in part by this rush of instant gratification that's about. It's not real stimulation, but it exhausts people to the point where joining in, in real life, is perhaps too difficult or beyond them. In part because imaginations get diminished through lack of experience."

"Like the staff discussing the characters on the TV shows at the care home as if they were intimate friends, but having difficulty even listening to me because I somehow didn't fit with their lot in life?"

"Sounds about right Tom. And we encourage each other to do it. And we are encouraged to do it in the culture that surrounds us. But I don't think it's the individual to blame for this behaviour. They have been robbed of the essence of confidence and curiosity by some harsher, more twisted sadness that comes from others and burrows into them. How often are we robbed of the time or the desire to listen to strangers or imagine something, anything involving ourselves? How often have you ever felt part of a community and not a fucking fan club? As soon as the conversation is begun you are given a shitty choice: either join in the script or you're not in. And this situation rules and ruins how many lives? Fucking fashionable misery my foot!"

"And you think that adds to peoples' insecurity?"

"One of the threads, yes. It also feels so much easier to push buttons on a screen that gives us insight into someone else's life, in a way that you can administer in doses. Instant effect, but superficial access to worlds you could otherwise never inhabit. And you know, the jump to pushing the button on a drill, or carrying plasterboard in the palms of your hands instead of a phone, is not so big. But the potential to be a real living, breathing part of building something for the community has innumerable rewards of a more tangible nature. A bit longer in terms of reaching the feeling, but one that makes an indelible vein within us; open us up to more than we were before."

"But that decision takes what, a sense of self-agency? And changing our approach to time?"

"Could call it that. Phone-brain has certainly shortened our attention span, completely fucks with your acceptance of the time-scale needed for creating something more meaningful."

"And the agency?"

"That brings up the fraud of definitions. Remember that *'care agency'* you worked for? The one that was taking 55% of what the care homes were paying for your wage. The one that threatened to fire you. The one that fucked up organising your

DBS check by not even submitting it. Then got you to fill in the paper work again because too much time had elapsed."

"Mate, but how does that connect to my self-agency?"

"Right. Excuse me. But these agencies are run for profit, not for people. What comes off the top goes somewhere else and you end up with diminished self-agency. You get less pay and you are abused by the situation ran for someone else's profit who couldn't give less of a fuck about care. And how could you ever challenge how these places are run on your own? It's impossible. You then end up having to work more and in precarious situations to make up the difference the agency takes from the first role. Thus, sticking you in a rut that takes away from your rights and self-agency."

"So, it's the feeling of being impotent? Not being able to think about the prospect of change or action because your exhausted and alone? I get that, but then you can add all the misery and the shit gossip you have to listen to because you're only there for a brief window of time." Thomas put down his cutlery and squeezed his hands between his knees. He gazed out of the window, before he continued, "and then it becomes a weird conversation, a race to the bottom or the worst experience someone has had. Complaints, everyone's mouths' full of complaints, but so seldom do they, or can they act on it."

"But there is always a possibility," said Peach.

"Doesn't feel like it," snapped Thomas.

"Perhaps not, because your sense of agency has been worn down, but it won't be forever that these organisations can run in this way. There will come a shift in attitude."

"Yeah, yeah. And my teeth are made of glass."

"His are, by the looks of it," Peach pointed at the guy at the end of the builders table and Thomas looked over his shoulder.

"You know, shifts come in so many forms. Like these people at the Buddhist centre at the bottom of the hill. Not everyone goes about claiming that Buddhism is the new self-help cure-all. But there are some. Wait, that's not where I wanted to go. Fuck. No." Peach started grasping at the air in front of him, as if trying to catch a falling leaf in an autumn wind. "Wait. There it is." He closed his fists tight. "Innsbruck. When I was still in Innsbruck, kicking around a bit looking for a job in late

November, I got offered some cash in hand to write a letter, in English, for a lady. We met each day over the course of the next week in the Hokus Pokus cellar bar. She would pay for everything, but I never accepted the offer of food from her. Her English came out in excited, sporadic bursts and she only heard a few of the questions I had to ask. It became clear, after the first ten minutes, that I was being involved in the strange, philosophical pursuit of a woman who felt entitled to knowledge, ennobled by her proximity to wealth.

"She was the estranged relative of a rich Friulian industrial family. Her teenage niece had committed suicide and she wanted to understand an aspect of the death. The girl in question had been, in the lady's description, strongly autistic – possibly what was once defined as Aspergus, or different. She was a lonely child, unloved by her gold digger step-mother who lost the attention of the tycoon father as soon as she, *became interesting*, which led to a hostile atmosphere in the family. Not one that the girl could grasp, but one that she felt the consequences of. She was intelligent, but had an acute social disdain for the pedantry of aristocratic family life. Not through conscious rebellion, purely through not being able to engage with the idiotic routines and spectacle that some families across Europe still entertain.

"She had grown attached to a computer tablet and enjoyed taking photographs and social media. She had an account for her photography and one day she got a comment from someone in London. A thread of communication began. She and this person began to go back and forth via the website, then emails, then phone calls. The niece refused to send pictures of herself naked to the other person when they asked and instead of discussing it with her family, or leaving the conversation, she began to ask why he wanted them. After a short while the person in London confessed an awful lot to this girl via email and text. Her persistent, yet innocent questions slowly drew out answers and she leant her ears to a paedophile who had had no other place to express himself so honestly and clearly and without reproach. He was given the chance to talk. He went beyond his sexual peculiarities and told her about his family life, about his sadness and his struggles at work.

"The conversations continued between them, until one of her cousins found out and held it over her as a secret. The man sent her pictures of his family and his house. He opened up to her, but her retreat from her own family life started a chain reaction. Her siblings from the step-family would pester her and make jokes about her and this man. She ignored them. Then, out of spite, her cousin told the step-mother about it.

She ignored it at first. That was, until it became leverage to get the attention of her husband; under the guise of motherly duty to the child. When the step-mother stole and refused to give the tablet back to the girl, she, in an act of rebellion, committed suicide.

"The pursuit of the woman I was sat across from was to understand why this man had opened up to this girl and to get him to answer the question why or how he had decided to tell her. So, she had hatched a plan to start the communication with him again, pretending to be the teenage girl. Pleading for his forgiveness, that her parents had taken her computer away and that she hadn't forgot him.

"She began giving me as much information as she could, showing me their emails and photos of him, his driver's licence, his diploma, his child. She told me there were two detectives following him, hired by her, as it was now believed he was part of a child sex network. The investigation was developing, but she wanted to find a way to talk to him before he was arrested. She wanted me to write a letter to him. To try and open up the conversation again. I think she had tried before, but with such a hostile tact that it was clearly no longer the niece talking to him.

"The family wanted nothing to do with it, or this lady, for the fear of shame it would bring to the business or the family name. There was never a fixed agreement, but I was paid 300 euros for that letter. The lady told me that the niece played the Clair de Lune by Debussy on the piano and that she had sent him a recording of it. I started there and carried on. The image of her, sitting at the piano, in the windowlight of a manor house near Trieste thinking of this man in London, still haunts me and I cannot listen to Debussy anymore.

"Two days after I gave her the letter -written on the elaborate stationary she'd purchased - she asked for more. For me to make a second copy and send it from England when I went back to visit my family. Then for me to make a third and travel to Deutschland and send it."

"But why send other copies?" Asked Thomas.

"I don't know mate. Her demands became more convoluted. I was wrapped up in the seeming absurdity of someone else's life. When I decided to step back from it and said I could help no more the story started to change; quickly. The detectives had arrested him somewhere in NW5. It was over for him and that she'd never find out now."

"Fucking hell," said Thomas, "but that's too fast an end. Isn't it? And where does all her money come from for this?"

"Diamonds mate, I think. She showed me all colour and size in these ornate boxes, but I don't know where they came from. It also became apparent to me that perhaps the whole thing was a game played on me by this woman. It all became a bit bizarre and Innsbruck became a creepy city, even more so because of the glare and sugar of the winter tourist trade of continental drunks and imported Chinese photographers that spilled over the streets. That's when I decided to get in touch with you to see what you were doing."

"But there's no shift."

"No, there is. It was in the teenager. She'd found a way to listen to this guy in a way that no one had before. She had avoided the taught reaction - to instantly demonise someone with a confronting addiction. By simply asking why, the teenager elicited self-reflection in the man; it provoked the potential for change. I'm not suggesting you pair up Asperger teenagers with all paedophiles. It's just a unique moment."

The West-Denton bus rolled down the hill outside the café. Peach and Thomas went into their own worlds. They stared at the café around them, not really engaging with any of it; just being present. Peach finished his coffee. The sound of the cup hitting the table pulled Thomas out of his reverie.

"Right. Mate, are you about ready to move?" Asked Peach.

"Yeah I'm done. So, how about the coast? From monument?"

"Yeah, I'll play the piano later. Evening rush hour is best for busking, even if that pratchy old woman moans at me for putting my hat down."

"Pratchy, what the fuck does that mean Peach?" Thomas smiled at his friend and offered to pay.

"What do you think?" Was all he replied.

They left the café. Thomas stopped to check he had everything with him. He looked at Peach waiting just down the street. His thin fingers shivering a little, shoulders bowed forward under his tattered coat and a grand grin upon his cheeks; behind him stood the city.

Chapter 4. Into Newcastle. The pockets of Peach's coat.

Over the cobbles of Sandhill in the Side, the junkies and prostitutes gambolled among the morning tourists. Taxis, driven by Nigerian professors, passed the delivery trucks that barrelled under the railway bridge. A young man rested a moment, sitting on the road sign beneath the arch and brickwork. He watched the traffic pass over the Tyne Bridge, the girders and metal struts so low to the roofs of the buildings in the Side they could be kissing. Asiatic couples, with eyes full of sleep-dust, lingered under the windows of Bessie Surtees house, with their cameras slung and inattentive. The street was still full of yesterdays' dregs. A wine bottle rolled beneath the window as they read from a passage in their guidebook: about how a young lover climbed out of her old life, into the arms of a suitor and soon to be landed politician; when the Side was a haven of despots, tax and trade, commerce and guilds, sails and unconcerned love. An errant spaniel sniffed around a bucket of narcissi bulbs outside a florist shop, pissed on them, then trotted off content.

Closer to the banks of the Tyne, the high-end smokehouses in Tudor shells opened their doors to air out the night before; the low-lit mussel bars and the menagerie come night club that reintroduced the human jukebox and the £15 glass of champagne stood quiet, closed up; empty.

The only boats that moored up here now were the charter tours or the private sloops and luxury yachts; waiting for the Millennium Bridge to rise or for custom. The riverside still had a Sunday market. Every weekend, the sickly toffee smell and bubbling cat shit coffee, kebabs and burritos, chilli oil and burnt sandalwood; reams of the stuff billowed and spooled around the gathered crowd, always pushing and busy, nosing around stalls of patchwork clothes, magnetic therapy bands, knock-off DVD's and baby blankets. The visitors and staff at the old Baltic flour mill, on the Gateshead bank, witnessing them before turning inwards. The buildings bowels, peppered with installations and exhibitions of modern art.

A fiscal-wise dealer - ex-serviceman with stories of Helmand province and the building of Camp Bastion- sloped past the boutique vinyl café on Sandhill road; preparing himself to push his BMX up the steep climb of Dean Street. The doors of a hotel near the bridge were cracked, police tape stuck on the splinters, from a morning raid. A case of tax evasion and profanity that may yet avoid the papers. A young mother walked, unbeknownst, past the dealer with his bike. She carried an apple in one hand and cradled her infants' head in the other; holding the child close in the folds of her Welsh wrap. She stepped past a blue walled Gentlemen's club and a microbrewery. A bouquet of bin bagged prophylactics, chain lube and hops lingered in the alley. People waited at the traffic lights where Dean Street became Grey, intersected by Mosley. Beyond the lights the franchise bistros and cafes flanked the ascent to Grey's Monument. The invariable offers and discount boards propped outside like candida chalked tongues, inside the boudoir blue and rouge mood lighting, enveloping electric candles, wax fruit and sweaty foul-mouthed kitchens. Grey Street, arced like a croupiers' deck, with the Theatre Royal on the corner of Market and Grey. Shakespeare street, up the south wall of the theatre; the stage door opposite Lady Grey's: the morning haunt of some retired and racist pension drunks, but with the shying of the light the sly and well-dressed strut like peacocks and bulge in glamourous dresses beneath Cornish green bottles and chandeliers as they swarm the bar; waiting for the weeks incumbent performers to emerge and distend with stories of the less romantic life of the arts. Out of the mouth of Shakespeare is Pilgrim Street. Two hydraulic pistons wheezed and snorted as a giant; steel jawed demolition machine pulled apart the New Bridge Project. The scars of the Odeon cinema were still there on the walls of Commercial Union House.

Tattoos of sliding brickwork and cracks in the pipes caused by the collapse of the cinema's façade into the street.

Through the dust beyond, the glass walls of the city library caught the morning light. On the sixth-floor balcony a young man sat sewing the lining of old bus chairs to a hairnet, to make a candy floss wig for a dancer. The echoes from of the fourth-floor computer suite filled the library with the shouts and shrieks of reeking drunks playing computer games next to people queuing up to ask for housing assistance, to type up care reports, and among them someone was practicing sign language at a computer screen in the vain hope of getting a job. Outside, Jimmy dropped off another box of mangos and mandarins at the fruit stall he ran at the bottom of Northumberland Street.

They arrived at Monument from Grainger street.

"Mate, I need the toilet."

"The Tyneside will be open by now. If you go up there, I'll wait for you outside Di Marco's."

"Fine." Thomas went up High Friar Lane, the sun reflected in the mirrored glass blinding him. He dipped inside the cinema and headed for the bar.

When he returned and stood at the end of High Friar Lane, he remained hidden in shadow for a moment. He watched Peach, sat with another coffee on a table outside, chatting with the waitress. Her hip pushed out, resting on his shoulder. Someone passing stopped to ask for a lighter. Peach fished one out of a pocket and carried on talking. Then a child from another table came over and asked the waitress for something. Peach gave her a sheet of paper from his notebook and a green colouring pencil from another. An elderly man appeared in the door and Peach handed him a book from his jacket pocket. A young couple on the street stopped and asked for something and Peach drew them a map. All the while chatting with the waitress. 'The world is inside the pockets of Peach's coat' thought Thomas before he crossed the street to join him.

"How is it that you've got everything in your pockets?" He asked as he sat beside Peach.

"Good question. Perhaps you should have some of this."

Peach pulled a couple dusty scraps of frankincense from a breast pocket and folded it inside Thomas's palm.

"This will help you keep calm. People have been using the perfume of this stuff to help settle their nerves for millennia."

"Why do I need it?"

"Have you seen your face this morning?"

Thomas stuck his tongue out. Peach paid up and they made their way down into the Metro station.

Chapter 5. Mountains. Memories. Making decisions.

Grandmothers milled about in leopard print tops, their jowls caked in foundation, jabbing at phones as they stood beside prams. One of the ticket barriers was broken and a repairman, with his stomach boiling out of his overalls, watched over the apprentices' shoulder as he pulled at the wires inside; offering his guidance as he shifted about on his feet. There was a security guard outside the supermarket. He was lean, but wore a kind expression on his face. Peach strode over to a ticket machine and went up on his toes, patting around on top.

"Looking for tickets?"

"Yep, sometimes they get left up here when they're not needed."

Peach found a couple out of date ticket stubs, but one was an all zone day rider bought and left earlier that morning. They split the change to pay for Thomas's ticket and headed down to the platform.

A young couple perched on the folding seat slabs, teasing each other's necks with kisses. A man, sat in a wheelchair, ate salt and vinegar crisps. Someone wrapped up in a hoody, sat huddled over, focusing on a hand-spinner that danced across his fingertips. A drunk swayed by the stairs, holding up his trousers with his free hand. The young gays, tucked into tight denim and wearing dyed contact lenses, leered at a magazine held between them. The yellow glossed bricks glowed under the lights. The soot black of the far wall – full of adverts for college enrolment schemes, last years' panto and the same vaping on a mountain of freedom campaign – was illuminated by the arriving train that followed the wind. Peach stared at the image of the mountain. The train arrived and they got on. He turned to his right, looking for a seat and saw the same advert in miniature running along the signage inside the carriage. He shuddered and sat down beside Thomas, staring out the back window of the Metro.

"Do you ever think you'll climb a mountain?"

"No Peach, probably not."

"Why not?"

"Well, lots of reasons," Thomas paused. The Metro slid towards Manners station. "I watched this documentary recently, about Everest."

"What was it about?"

"About Everest you tit. It was about the collapse of an ice shelf that fell in 2014. It killed sixteen Sherpa. Really well-made documentary. They started with the family of the lead Sherpa for one of the tour groups. His wife was unhappy with how obsessed her husband had become with climbing. He was going for a record, something like twenty-two trips to the summit. Twenty-two. And then they introduced the tour operator. Who seemed, in essence, to defy the way the Sherpa thought about Everest."

"How do they think about it?"

"According to them it is part of Mother earth. It is a very important part of their world view. And the tour 'operator' swaggered about with this massive blind spot. He was part of the process of exploitation. He always referred to the Sherpa's as 'boys.' People pay over forty thousand pounds to be on these tours, and so, part the way up Everest are these base camps with a fucking TV, bookcases, sofa chairs. It's obscene."

"Because I've got money, I can do the things."

"Yeah, that's pretty much how it looks. Then, after the avalanche, the deaths and the strikes and a visit from the passive minister for tourism, the tour 'operator' has the audacity to try and explain the situation to the tourists, claiming that his Sherpa, fucking 'his' Sherpa, are being threatened with violence by the other Sherpa. It's complete bullshit."

"And is there any recognition of that?"

"Yes, by someone who works in the Nepalese ministry. And now, a couple years later, they're talking about the excess of human waste and rubbish on the side of Everest. People dying in queues to reach the summit. It's odd."

"Yes Tom, a bit peculiar."

"But, how easily can people be duped?"

The Metro emerged from the tunnel at Manners. The walls went up to the sky and Thomas followed them upwards with his gaze. The train cleared the ascent from the sunken station. Thomas fell silent for a minute and watched the city, as they arced over the Byker Bridge. As they came into the Byker station he continued.

"One of the people sympathised with the Sherpa, and was filmed saying so to Sherpa, but wasn't interviewed. The other people interviewed were so self-interested and upset because they couldn't fulfil their dreams. One guy from the group started calling the Sherpa terrorists, seemingly going along with the lies given by the git who ran the tour company. In the struggle to commit to self-interest one is often prepared to accept all kinds of lies."

"Totally, and there is the start of the holy trinity of 21st century deception: terrorists, tourists and what else?"

"Good question. Traps? Paralogizing know-alls? Singing like choir sheet crowds, deceiving themselves through a learnt logic that masks the insecurity of not knowing. Making someone else's false arguments and thinking it's your own opinion. In the pursuit of defining and knowing everything, we have lost sight of the joy of inquiry, of curiosity."

"I guess it gets really dangerous when the sense of self and your own identity becomes dependent on these things. It means any challenges to the logic of what you say are received as an attack on the self. It's upsetting because it means the identity becomes dependent on such a narrow and rigid understanding of the world. And it's so hard to defend most arguments or opinions – because they don't really make sense, and yet they are what we have made ourselves out of."

Peach leaned in.

"There are these little experiments, something me and my dad concocted a while back," said Peach. "We have a theory that people have slowly loosened their grip on their own free will, that they have offered their choices to external actors, so there is no risk that they take that is truly their fault if it fails or goes wrong. They have given up or been robbed of their responsibilities in life. We want to offer people moments to act that encourage them to make their own choice. To be in themselves and to decide for themselves, based on the world around them.

"An example from my father, who travels a lot for work, comes from Beijing airport. He had given a lecture at the university there and was on his way home. The university had got him a business class ticket which entitled him to use the lounge before flying. He doesn't normally accept the business class tickets, but there is a culture of pride and façade in China. In the lounge he had free food, free drink, crèche space for children, beds, showers, prayer room and the rest. And as part of this luxury you get a guest, one guest per business ticket. My father, sat at the bar with his coffee, struck up a conversation with a middle-aged man, in some industry or other who was heading to Dubai. They looked around at the relatively quiet lounge and my father put it to him that they could go to the other passengers and ask if anyone was hungry or needed prayer space or use of the facilities because they could bring in, between them, two guests. They finished their drinks and walked down to the gate. Together, two complete strangers walked around each passenger, briefly explaining the situation. All on equal terms, the single mothers with children, the backpackers; the older passengers; everyone that was sat waiting."

"Did anyone accept their offer?"

"Not one, they sat there, most of them in silence my dad said, or they politely declined. When they boarded the plane, my dad and this fellow stranger sat near each other in the business class and all the other passengers had to board by walking through. As they passed through, some of them apologised to my father, they said that they had been a little suspicious of the offer."

The Metro sank into the tunnel. Their faces appeared on the window, stretched and warped under the lights in the carriage.

"I'd thought at least someone would have accepted the offer," added Thomas, lifting his hand to test his cheek against the bulge in the reflection.

"You'd think so, but it makes me wonder. Even this backpacker declined. Begs the questions of how tightly defined his assumptions have become. Who gives him these impressions of other people? Who guides his prejudice or acceptance of another person? Perhaps he's had a really bad experience with people in business suits, perhaps. But if his suspicions are given to him by someone else, then it lets this external narrator suck away at this young man's opportunity to engage with life." Peach turned to Thomas, who stopped prodding his cheeks and leaned back from the glass.

"Like a leech?"

"Yes, Tom. Like a fucking leech. At the airport my father would have been wearing a business suit, having come straight from the lecture. Does that suit equate to being 'one of them?' Does the backpacker understand only himself to be the cultured, karmic "Us" of the alternative to the capitalist, business-suit wearing "Them" antagonists? If so, then that mind set is flawed. Like the hippies were, when they were prime consumers, the logic of the liberal individual is wrought within the framework and language of a hegemony, and is in fact, not an alternative at all. That he could not see, or was not willing to look beyond the suit suggests, this whole 'us and them' divide is a farce really. And both scary and tragic that such a deeply flawed idea of the self could dictate his response to a unique offer from a stranger – who knows what could have stemmed from that interaction! The language and logic of the 'us and them' dichotomy, as the supposed counterculture breeds into its disciples, continues the perpetual revolution, going round in circles, because that's all a revolution is, just finding ever more elaborate and vibrant ways to search for their own arse."

The light of day cleared their reflection off the Metro window.

"The Western culture, or perhaps I can only speak of the British, liberal culture," continued Peach in a deeper timbre, "has made a bastard of such ideas as Karma. That they use it as an excuse for a phenomenon, passive, almost cynically, rather than in an active sense, participating in it."

The Metro arched into the corner, curving round towards the Chillingham road station. The surveillance graffiti on the corrugated iron warehouse walls, rusted railway sleepers, wiry branches of still dead acorn trees, the expanse of tracks that branched out beyond the treeline – where by night the carriages were scrubbed and disinfected by grandfathers from Tajikistan and Polish aunties – covered by the shadow of the Seimans factory; the buckled paunch of kicked in wire fences; the dirty station platform. Always this same defeated mosaic, prying and taunting the subjective mind.

Peach shuddered.

As a younger man, he met someone who lived over on First Avenue, just the other side of Chillingham road; behind the Metro station. It became an established fact of life that, if Peach was going to piss off anyone or fuck up in front of someone, it turned out to be in front of her. In front of Rita.

By coincidence she was a friend of Mary's. She had been introduced to Peach by Thomas somewhen in the West Midlands before she also moved North for work. Much to Peach's misfortune, she was from Yorkshire and held her grudges. She was unimpressed by him and expressed it each time they met.

Considering some of the more aggravating moments it was not surprising. He had passed out, knackered and drunk - after a month's work as a dogs-body for an absurd theatre company - in his car at four a.m., with the music blaring, in front of her parents' house after dropping Mary off; he then argued with her father who hammered on the windows, before falling asleep in their garden. Another time, he turned up with a suitcase to the house on First Avenue to cheer up one of her housemates who he knew from an earlier visit. Peach and the housemate had been out for the evening and had returned home to carry on drinking. While his friend was pouring the wine, he had pulled a dead mackerel from the suitcase and slapped him with it – it turned into a frenzied, chaotic fight that meant fish scales and stomach scum where found seven months later behind the cooker. After being banned from the house, he had turned up one night when Rita was out and fallen asleep in the living room – whilst he believed he had in fact left and walked home – then proceeded to raid the fridge in a stupor before wandering off into the fog of mid-winter Byker. There were more misdemeanours, perhaps embarrassments by comparison. However, the tension between the two of them had eased; mainly because they hadn't seen each other for a while.

Sometimes it is a good idea to step away.

Since those years Peach had acquired a more thoughtful disposition, somewhat less self-destructive. He pushed his nose against the cool of the window and stared at the passing freight train. He had never considered giving up alcohol before, but the idea was dancing in his thoughts of late. As far as drugs went, it had a foul and ruinous and boring effect on people. What had really kicked his shins about it was a night at Central Station. He had gone to play the piano, but instead found a bunch of well dressed, cantankerous piss-heads who were kicking and thrashing it. A fight broke out, but the police intervened and just threw them all back into the night.

He had set a date to decide on, St Lucy's feast day. To carry on or for no more to ever pass his lips. He felt it was the best way for him, but that day might come sooner – the calendar is only an approximation of reality. His addictive, salacious nature and nuances wouldn't allow for him to create a moderate balance. As with most things for Peach, and with his life, it was either everything or nothing. He swam between these points on the continuum, inviting the manic phases that accompanied an indulgence in either to the point of excess. In his mind, by accepting one – instead of both at the same time – he was offering himself another way to approach his habit. He kept this decision to himself, feeling it germinate inside of him, knowing a change would come to pass.

He pulled his nose back from the window and turned to Thomas.

"So, too, the idea of spontaneity has been defined in a dangerous sense, bordering on reckless behaviour."

They heard a shout as the doors closed. A gang of teenagers swung their legs over the fences and ran, while a group of young women ran down the slope to try and reach the train. Neither of them made it and the sound of them beating the Perspex soon faded as the Metro carried on towards the coast.

A woman, clutching a phone, lurched in the aisle. She flailed, but managed to grab a guard rail. She smelt of white lightning cider, stolen perfume and fried potatoes. She glared at everyone while listening to the phone, before exploding in response with a gossiped volley of 'lock the cunt out and Claire's a fucking thief' that filled the carriage. Peach and Thomas let her be and carried on watching the world through the back window. The lady stepped out at Wallsend. She forced a young couple to split to let her through. They came together again and found a seat together, holding a little closer to one another as they did.

Out the back window two girls in black tracksuits waved to their friends. As the Metro left the platform they looked around before stealing a kiss from another. Then they were too far away.

Peach rolled a knuckle of frankincense in his pocket. He broke off a nub and held it up to his nose. He rubbed it on the collar of his coat before putting it back in a different pocket.

He clapped his hands together and the resin dust hung in the air. He breathed out and watched it settle on window ledge.

"There was a couple I once met in Thailand that had followed me over the Malaysian border."

"When were you in Thailand Peach?"

"When I was living in Malaysia, in Kota Bharu – peculiar that it translates to Newcastle and is also in the North East of the country near a border – someone I once went to school with got in contact with me. He was living in Bangkok, working as an English language teacher. It was when I left England, a couple years ago."

"Ah, after Annie?"

Peach ignored Thomas's question.

"He invited me up to visit and I agreed. I booked a hostel in a city halfway up country to break up the journey. When I got to Rantau Panjang, the border town, I used my scant Malay to ask for directions. I set off towards the checkpoint. About a hundred metres behind me was the couple. They were also behind me at passport control, but did not reply when I said hello in a couple of different languages. I saw them again on the train, in the first-class seats when I passed through to get to the kitchen carriage.

"That evening when we pulled into Hat Yai I began walking towards the hostel I'd sorted out. I turned around and saw them again, following me. I kept walking, but by this point they were pretty much beside me. I stopped and asked if they were staying in the same hostel as me, 'No, we just followed you because you looked like you knew where to go.' I shit you not. They were fortunate there was a room in the hostel. They asked to join me to go and look for food. Curious, I agreed.

"They were on their way to the party islands, dressed in the prescribed parachute pants and hessian shirts. Devendra, the guy I was living with in Kota Bharu, and I, used to joke that they were handed out at the Thai airports like the Lai in Hawaii."

"What party islands?"

"Essentially, white man's paradise for the modern colonials: drugs, beaches, parties. In short consumable hedonism. I asked what they would like to eat when we found somewhere to sit down, they didn't care so I ordered three of the same. He ate it and she picked it apart, dowsing the spice with beer. On the walk back to the hostel they told me all about what they wanted to do in their escapist fantasy.

"I left Hat Yai a day early to get away from them. The rest of the train journey was a sensory wonder. To witness sunrise over the Siamese jungle from the open back door and on the running steps of an early twentieth century carriage is bliss. During the night, I found the skeletal structure of a dragonfly near my seat. I held the golden and delicate form in my hand, turning it about in the carriage light. As I watched the light play on the body, I got to thinking, and worrying a lot about these spontaneous liberal travellers."

"Why?" Asked Thomas.

"Something that happened in the kitchen carriage on the first train up to Hat Yai."

"What happened?"

"When Devendra and I were living in Kota Bharu there had been a series of bombing raids taking place close to the border, bitterness and dissatisfaction leads some people to violence. There was even one in Bangkok that my friend from Kota Bharu got caught in the blast of, but survived. All this violence creates a tension that causes a reaction, and so, on the train was a pretty big military presence. Some in camouflage, some in plain green, some in black. I'm not sure what the differences meant, but they were all armed.

"I walked into the kitchen carriage for a coffee. The soldiers sat at the table across from me and watched as I rolled a cigarette. I noticed the attention the kitchen porter was giving me so I followed his eyes, the soldiers were watching closely. I figured his gaze meant, don't do anything stupid, or at least too stupid. So, I didn't."

"Can you smoke on the trains?"

"Yes, and wind the windows down to breathe, unlike our civilised nightmares here, but I digress. One of them, with a score of regal badges across his breast and a fancy hat, kept nudging the soldier next to him; who eventually came over to me. He put his gun on the table in front of me and pulled out his own tobacco and dried leaves. We spoke in a broken language, more gesture and noise than words. Turned out, they wanted to show me how to roll with bamboo leaves instead of the papers I had. He showed me and we smoked together. What I took to be the general or the person of seniority started laughing. As it is my nature, I clowned around a bit, in body language, why not make them laugh a little?

"As I sat back down the soldier lent over the table with a small polly pocket tin. He opened it and it was crammed full with strong, Cambodian weed. None of the soldiers flinched or even paid attention, they carried on as they were, but this one kept insisting I had some."

"And?"

"Mate, I might be a folk devil and I have seen moral panic that envelops the planet, but I'm no one's fool. Imagine if I had accepted? In a time when Siamese nationalists are wrestling to get the independence of their culture back, to step away from a reliance on tourism, when the bombings had taken place at 'Western' hotspots. I was 'one of those Westerners', in someone's eyes, as I sat on a train heading North the week after a large bomb exploded in Bangkok. To accept the weed would have been ludicrous. Direct to jail, direct to media coverage for political leverage or to be baptised as the next scapegoat. Not for me. Besides, I don't smoke it anymore anyway. But as I sat there staring at the dragonfly wings during the night and then staring out over the herons in the rice fields in the morning, I thought about those two that had followed me. Imagine if they'd been sat there, not me?"

Thomas looked hard at his friend, searching for the evidence of not smoking weed anymore. Perhaps there was no way to prove it, but his eyes were a bit richer in colour.

"But, would they have even been sat there, Peach?" Thomas interrupted. "What's the likelihood they would even talk to the guards in the first place? They were in the first-class seats; they had no need to talk to anyone else. They weren't in Thailand, they were heading *to* Thailand, by the sounds of it. Maybe Thailand only exists, when they reach the party island? Maybe Thailand only exists when they've ticked off another hotspot, or seen something that is nestled amongst the pages of the guidebook?"

"Perhaps, but aren't they supposed to be the charismatic, freewheeling personalities that are part of these alternative lifestyles?"

"It is just a fantasy of an alternative lifestyle. Fashionable and curated. The fantasy has no risk once you're inside the bubble; the tour is guided, unless you end up on the wrong beach. The need to manage risks is not part of the trip. They would not be in the kitchen carriage mate. By not being in the conversation with the guard, or even with you – on the journey to the island – they stave off the slip into bad faith. However, it broke down at one point when they started following you and you saw how tired they were and the dirty knickers beneath the fur. It's difficult, for all of us, imagine having to develop a personality between the extremities of egotism and anxiety and keep a straight face the whole time. That someone or something else offers to take the risk into consideration for you to make life easier, is alluring, but granted it's got us in a mess that the late Ulrich Beck and Mr Giddens warned us about in the 90's."

Thomas had been fond of risk theory. Apart from stimulating cynicism, some aspects of Sociology are invaluable. Peach had once given him a copy of Beck's Risk Society as a birthday gift after a stint as an informal academic assistant. His hope had been that Thomas would see how a chance idea or encounter for one could create a different perspective lens for another.

"Makes sense," replied Peach. "and if you look at society as the management and economy of risks you really ought to develop your individual capacity for will power instead of deferring the responsibility to another person or organisation. If not, there is a sad comedy in the Lonely Planet tour guide books. It's also like red meat."

"What the fuck are you talking about? Red meat?"

"If you ask someone why they eat red meat, which I had to do for a research assistant role I had, most of the time you'll get one of four fallible responses: 'my family does it, my culture eats it, I've always eaten it or I don't know enough about the alternatives'. All are fallible in logic because all of these positions require defending, but are indefensible by the individual because in none of them has that person used their own reasoning, they're paralogizing. Ask them again with a little more emphasis on the word 'you' and you begin to trigger an ego response, they become defensive or aggressive, but undefinably so. Red meat diets, on the scale of today, are unsustainable and they require the individual giving up their control of risk. The supermarket decides what is safe and not always based on its adherence to legislation from food standards agencies and other bodies. This leads to an ever decreasing right or control that an individual has over their own source of sustenance. The allusion is hidden by the question of choice on a shelf. And if the individual doesn't understand why they eat red meat, how could they be capable of engaging with decisions made on their behalf on a political level?"

"That's a bit of a jump Peach."

"But is it? It's the same situation, if you peel back the gauze and rhetoric that holds together someone's connection to one explanation or other for why they choose one party or another, do you receive a sincere answer?"

"What about people who make informed decisions?"

"If an individual makes an informed decision, they are using the capacity for reason, I am not contesting that here. But, at enumerable points in this culture of ours, we are asked and encouraged to defer our right to reason for ourselves, instead, repeating to oneself the same flawed logic; hardening with each repetition. Our energy pours into arguments about the symptoms of our culture, never confronting the debilitating flaws that perpetuate the status quo. Any culture driven by male ego, principles of dominance or superiority, and an inability to accept its own mistakes, is bound to leave its citizens cynical and apathetic. Such a consuming worldview hinders our ability to step back, breathe, accept the reality for what it is, and think, 'what can we do next?'

The train had gone quiet, the only sound was the rhythmic clicking of the joins in the train tracks, lulling all into a moment of reflection.

"It is also", Peach said, breaking the silence, "boring as fuck."

—

Back in the East end, a man from Syria drove his taxi across Byker Bridge, ferrying a young man to work in High Heaton. As they crossed the bridge, they saw seven people together, all looking over the railings.

"Beneath them is the Ouseburn and beyond is the Tyne, if you asked each of them people what they saw they would find a different detail, attention drawn by their state of mind and experiences in life. All are right in what they observe and they can cooperate in their descriptions," said the driver to the young man.

"And if you can get everyone to agree they see the circle, you can show them it as a coiled spring when you turn it to a new perspective, loaded with centuries of tension that they are holding onto knowingly or without knowing. The easiest and hardest action is to let go, to watch the tension force the spring up, shattering the circle into a new state. Much like Murakami described his love of pinball machines. Once you let go, change begins and you cannot stop it."

Chapter 6. Metamorphosis on the Coast. Meditation. Relief.

They stepped off at Tynemouth, beneath the sun burnt glass and Victorian ironwork canopies; wrapped, for a moment, in the silence shared between brothers in thought.

The station, too, was quiet. No one sat outside the café. The waitress busied herself with cleaning the tables and staring out the window. A lady in a burka and bright white trainers checked the timetable, whilst a young man with a shaved head and "claks" tattooed across his fingers watched her, adjusting the collar on his postal shirt.

Peach and Thomas stepped outside the station. Both drew in a breath, that pulled the taste of the North Sea air a little closer. They breathed out.

"Better?"

"Much ta'.

Front street smelt of the chocolatier's experiments in the corner shop, warped by the stale beer and fag ash that lingered on the curb side like pages of history. A quartet of thin teenagers, wearing black T-shirts full of fashionable rebel slogans, strolled out of the Co-op; each holding a two-litre bottle of cheap cider. Loners milled about, watching people park their cars or gazing at the middle-aged women walking into the boutique bars. Peach and Thomas crossed over and walked past Marshall's fish and chips shop - the gangway within already full with the lunch-seekers. As they turned down the stairs, towards King Edwards Bay, an old man took his rest on a bench. His veined and ruddy cheeks stood out above a black and white knitted scarf. Next to him sat a glam-queen teenager taking pictures of herself.

"I have begun to wonder, Tom, that perhaps we need a willing listener that can act as a trigger in a conversation that gives shape to a thought we were trying to draw together out of fragments."

"Agreed."

"Same too, I suppose, goes for trying to make sense of the culture around us, but having become overwhelmed by it, it requires a bit of an influence - a provocation perhaps. Though different from how a drug has an influence over your thoughts and perception; more like how a coincidence or a chance encounter can change our perspective. These moments that can reveal something much bigger and sometimes a lot more familiar than what we see and *know*. I had been seeking conversation and perspective and I found it among people."

"Are you in a period of reflection Peach?"

"Yes, I suppose I am. Talking to you helped with the ordering of my thoughts."

"You're welcome Peach."

Thomas caught Peach as he slipped on a cracked step.

"Thanks. I am getting better at dispelling my frustration, this confusion over how to make myself clear. The pieces of it are all bobbing around, idle yet charged in my thoughts and actions, waiting for some kind of spark or shunt. Interaction can be a good thing in this respect."

"Or perhaps you just needed to shoot your mouth off enough," said Thomas, digging his knuckle into Peach's ribs.

A couple approached them on the steps. Both in their early 30's, tired eyes and a bit pale-cheeked from the winter's darkness, both communicating through a silent grace and care for one other; the way he moved aside to make the way easier for her as they climbed; the soft touch she applied to his shoulder. Beneath his jacket he wore a wrap with a child swaddled inside. A cry from a gull overhead drew a shriek of laughter from the infant. The father glanced at Peach as they passed. Their eyes met and, in a sense, they knew each other in the moment and shared a smile because of the infant's eruption.

"It's as if I know the crucial aspect of it, but-" began Peach after the couple passed, but was cut off by Thomas.

"What? That under all of this, the essence of everything in existence is to interact; to collaborate?"

They paused on the steps.

"Yes, Tom. There it is," Peach levelled his hand with the blur between North Sea and the sky, tracing the seam with his fingers as if across the keys of piano. "That *is* it. And how do we approach this metamorphosis of perspective? Through force? Through violence? Through dictating to people what they should and shouldn't do? You fucking what mate? Have such approaches ever worked?

"We have been worn down, disfigured; turned into an island of individuals and forced into a competition for an ever-diminishing slice of the cake. We are encouraged to step on one another in order to fulfil the modern fantasy of honest reward for honest effort. But it is *this* that is killing us!

"That is why I propose a change in the ruling aspect of society, from competition to collaboration. It would be a starting point for whatever comes next. We could tell our children different stories, sing different love songs, we could play new games. Perhaps we could even let go of our fear of death and embrace the great unknown with a curious reverence. Society is a human project; to be worked-on and refined; not controlled. And we are all here to join in, beginning with the things we have around us right now."

They stepped onto the bay, the tide receding before them, and began walking towards the rocks beneath the priory.

"Do you reckon you can build something using faulty tools though?"

"What do you mean?"

"Well if you try and use what we've got, to build something new out of what's already here, aren't we just going to end up with more of the same?"

"I don't think so, mainly because the aim at the beginning is simply to introduce a small change in peoples' perspective. To gently awaken their imaginations that could lead to a massive shift in how they interact with the world. I don't want people to jump and scream 'let's rebuild, smash this and burn them…' That kind of rebellion requires an enemy, manufactured or otherwise. Besides, it's not about building anything new with old tools."

"What is it then?"

"It's about no longer propping up what has been started with those tools – the banking system, the merchant economy, the welfare state, the care industry, public transport; the list is long – these institutions that were not maintained or developed for the betterment of people. In the name of efficiency, they have been worn down by private interest and the pursuit of money. How about stopping, reflecting, then considering how to travel, how to care, how to exist, how to live under a different value system. If we believed that human nature was collaborative, not competitive." He paused and pinched his bottom lip between his teeth. "Then acting on it."

"These grand social experiments and the powers-that-be, that've unfurled in such a rude and disfigured way, aren't just shit on the street Peach. It would be impressive if people could be reminded of what these pillars of society were supposed to be for." Thomas pulled his arms around his chest, trying to warm himself against the fresh wind coming off the sea. "But, in part, I agree with you. Look at the role of social care. It, quite simply, should not be thought of as an industry. The concept of care has mutated by wavering stewardship, caught up in profit incentives that barely consider the actual *humans* who are in need, their vulnerabilities and experience of life. There are so many of these social practices – care, hospitality, counselling, – that should not have to expend half their energy struggling to survive. Competition denies the possibility of equal rights for all in these regards."

"Yes. And some small changes to our social language could put the world together in a slightly different way, revealing the cracks in competitive culture to everyone, and invite us all to see what, perhaps, could live instead."

Peach gazed up at the ancient holes in the walls of the priory. He placed both hands onto the cliff and pushed, stretching his legs out behind him. Thomas watched until his attention was caught by a chunk of blue glass, smoothed by the salty water; half sunk into the sand.

"Can you remember the anarchists from down Bristol way?" asked Peach, rhetorically. "They took the family ferry crossing coupons from that conservative, bile-gloom tabloid and helped bring back stranded families from the Calais Jungle camp and home them in protective communities in the south-west. It is this kind of gesture. The next step would be a complete metamorphosis."

"Peach. You're jumping again. Just because you've said it twice now, it doesn't make any more sense. Should we go up the Long sands, to St Mary's?"

They turned to face the north. The cold waters washed over the empty bay. Peach kicked up tufts of sand. He knew this stretch of the coast well. When he first came to visit Thomas, he would come out here by night and swim naked beneath the full moon. On another occasion, in the middle of a Tuesday morning, he had waded into the North Sea, dressed in his ragged suit, carrying demijohns that he had filled with salt water to make a bath for Thomas; to help his skin. He came out here and sat with his sadness and grief and his small joys. He came out here to sit in the wind on the rock that jutted out from the grassy knoll that the pair were now climbing over.

"Towards the lighthouse? Fine. Well, no. Yes, you're right. That is a bit of a jump."

"Thank you."

"I just get excited is all," he stuffed his hands into his pockets, reaching for his tobacco. He felt the pouch under his fingers. Thomas carried on towards the shoreline. Peach let go of it and caught up. "How about this? Do you know what Bricolage is?" he asked.

"No."

"No problem. Did you ever face a problem, and the only way to solve it was to improvise with the materials at hand?"

"Yes, for sure. No example comes to mind, but I know I've done it."

"Well, that's the essence of Bricolage. When I was helping in the theatre for example. Anytime I had to dismantle something and take those parts and put them together in a different way, to satisfy other needs - that's Bricolage. When there's a health crisis or a virus and we have to look at each other and every surface in a new way. To take the coupons from the paper and use them for a different purpose is an action influenced by this idea. And it's that skill, one that I reckon all of us have used at some point, that is instrumental to a metamorphosis, to transform the practices and institutions we have now."

"Fair enough. Might be a struggle for those who fear change though. Or who've learnt to think that they aren't creative."

"Fearing change does not isolate oneself from its effects. We cannot escape the consequences of social change because we are all directly or indirectly connected. With all the forms of communications possible now we can engage with this idea of Bricolage and apply it to these old institutions and begin to turn them on their head."

"Even in England?"

"Of course, and it's part of the humour in the possibility of a *Conservative* future. It's a contradiction, but also a scary possibility. But think on this, what course of action is more productive? To collaborate with others to create a new option, or to rally behind an opposition that narrates its own impotence and unwillingness to change as if it were comprised of only highly-intelligent and well-educated rhetoric?"

Thomas clambered over the rocks, whereas Peach strode with confidence. The tangy smell of the sea grass fused with the salt water and covered their jackets with spray. Thomas put his hand down in gull shit. He washed it off in a rock pool.

"I suppose," he said, putting his hands in his pockets to dry.

"Well, look at it this way. Those teenagers from earlier, down by the Co-op. They know the vague *something* that they are against. They've got it on their t-shirts - probably in their headphones too, slogans always *anti* or *against*. The political Left has been dragged into that position, all of their oxygen going to talking about the very thing they are in opposition to. And, unfortunately, it is this position that is manipulated by certain information and culture makers to create the Left as a mere extreme opposite to what exists."

"And what, what would you suggest to those teenagers?"

"I propose for a generation to be *'for'* something in its entire ethos, no longer accepting of the negative 'against' position. Rising against, raging against the machine, anti-capitalist, the Steppenwolf; this is the narrative of a subservient position. Instead, to have a subtle shift into positive, collaborative action. For example, if the wealth inequality fuck's them off so much they could instead focus on a barter or gift economy and actually *practice* it or join an intentional community that already uses it. If not, all of this anti-posturing helps support the very thing it is in opposition to, reenforcing the status quo it speaks of destroying."

"But if you challenge the protective layer that people have built around themselves," added Thomas, "they'll lash out at you. And if it's protective why would you let go of it easily? If it all falls away, you become vulnerable."

"Yes, but being vulnerable, in some regards, allows us to be open to change. Many of us have to learn that lesson. Men especially, who for generations have been taught: *'you have to be hard, tough, stolid - fixed in that role'*. To be vulnerable is to be fluid. But if it's fluid then it cannot really be controlled. And if it cannot be controlled then it is a nuisance or a danger to this culture that needs a clearly-defined opposition to maintain its own sense of authority."

The bay disappeared behind them, before them the Longsands. The grubby sandstone of St George's church loomed over the far end of the beach, on the invisible divide between Tynemouth and Cullercoats. Along the street were the decayed plastic dinosaurs in the amusement park and the squat Aquarium building. There were a few young parents out with prams on the beach, at times getting stuck between sand and the pebbles. A woman was dragged along by the five dogs she was holding. She dug in her heels, unchained them all and let them fly around the beach and into the surf.

"To stand always against something is, in a sense, to be as the priest in Paris said, one of the people to stand only to be photographed; to be a participant in the spectacle of opposition rather than an active contributor. I am not standing against modern hypocrisy: I am standing for the metamorphosis of human collaboration. We have stood against modern hypocrisy so long it has diminished our imaginations and sullied our self-belief.

"To broaden out the example, the question that periodically gets thrown around, for Feminism to be radical, what does that mean? Is it adapting to the need to change instead of stagnating? Or is it similar to the piece of graffiti by Banksy, of the subcultures lining up to buy the destroy capitalism t-shirt? Did you see that one?"

"No. I'll look for a picture of it later."

"Ok. So, you don't have to look too far back in the history of Feminism, and we find that Edward Bernays, under the direction of George Washington Hill, co-opted a large part of the Feminist wave by selling them cigarettes, to be used as 'torches of freedom' in defiance, against the norm that women were not allowed to smoke. In that action he expanded the size of the market for cigarette companies and helped to influence a part of the waves' narrative."

"But, how does that make it flawed?"

"When an argument begins under the language of the oppressor – of the master, as Camus put it – you're locked into that struggle. This period of history, for the Feminist movement, was not the great inclusive community it is now, and by smoking their cigarettes it got drawn into the consumer cycle. And the chance for something creative, I mean truly creative – not just redressing the wounds in a fabulous manner – to support women, was lessened. Feminism is an incredible social power, the potential inherent within the movement is immense and it will continue to grow. And, in many places, it has outgrown this part of itself. It addresses what is most vulnerable and grows through it."

"Undoubtedly."

"Yeah, and if you had a strength of women…"

"Is that a collective noun?"

"Could be. If you had a strength of women developing social care projects, housing benefits or work schemes, a lot of British culture could be very different." Peach reached into his pocket, but pulled nothing out. "I wonder," he continued "what could it be in the future? As part of the metamorphosis over the next decade, perhaps after the pendulum has swung so far the other way, will we have communities of humans or maybe we'll have…"

"A completely different word instead of humans by then."

"Maybe! Can you imagine… what we could be?"

"This morning, I can't imagine," said Thomas, rolling his shoulders to ease an ache beneath his shoulder blades. He held his arm across his chest and stretched as they walked. A brief smile rose on his lips, he had long enjoyed their shared fondness for playing with words.

"Yeah, but isn't that exciting? You know, speculation is also creation."

"Not when you're exhausted or a financier."

"There! Exhaustion! If you have to make substantial decisions when you're exhausted, how is it possible to come up with a decent solution or something different to what you know? It's impossible." Peach rested his hand on the outside walls of St George's as they paused for a moment. "That's partly what these old religions have come to functions as. They have become a catch all belief to provide answers to stress and exhaustion, instead of inspiring human unity."

"Or like modern technology being the saving grace?"

"Or conspiracy theories."

"Exactly, neither of us are philistines, nor luddites, but an even more excessive addiction to technology in the future scares me."

"But,"

"But what? It's true. Look at mobile phones, great for communicating across distances. Multi-functional wonder-tools of the 70's superhero style. But the advertising and marketing and manufacturing of these things comes at such a human and ecological cost, with so little attention to the consequences of using them, yet they are engrained in everyday life and how we think the future will look. It is the bastardisation of interconnectivity. And where is the reflection on whether it's a good idea? Where's the choice? Everyone's got one so we all have to use them, if not you struggle, or need a really strong community around you. Reliance on them is proven to be unhealthy. It allows for the social world to fragment, accelerate and retard all at the same time. It's so limiting and degenerative that it makes me believe the species is governed by the impulse of a seven-year-old boy in a tantrum."

Somewhere beyond the church sat a terrace row. Rehousing schemes introduced in the area meant ex-convicts or young families or people who needed assisted living dwelt now beside the sea. The garden beds on the grass opposite lay turned, but empty.

"Yeah, sounds about right," said Thomas.

They walked along in silence for a while. As they reached the end of the Longsands, Peach led Thomas over the rocks and towards Cullercoats Bay. The sun caught on the pools, blinding them and the slime of the seaweed underfoot slowed them down. Peach pulled off his boots, carrying them at his side instead.

"And how often do these 'alternative' groups demand that you conform?"

"What? Why are we talking about alternative groups now?" Asked Thomas, as he recalled Peach's tendency to return to his own thoughts without telling the person he was speaking with.

"Well, it's kind of the end of an earlier thought I had. In so much that, there are characteristics of the demonised Capitalist in the 'anti' movement." He clenched his fists and released them. "What I meant was that a myriad of 'alternatives' and their definitions are, mostly, decided by a status quo that relies on binary language structures. The 'us' and 'them' dialogue, to put all of life in the terms of 'black' or 'white', it can be argued that one's ability to perceive an 'alternative' to the present culture is limited, if not impossible."

"In what way? That we reduce our experience of the world to this binary?"

They rounded on the next bay, clambering up the shoulder of the sea wall to walk along its spine.

"If the language we use is structured to enshrine competition, then our minds must shift to untangle our language from present culture. Language is a pillar of our collective humanity; to see it being so thoroughly abused makes me sad. For

135

example, when you see the word awesome being used, or even fucking copyrighted, to describe processed meat or a lump of plastic with flashing lights. But I digress. To accept the mechanics and consequences of competitive culture, and the monster it has become, would be the first step in pivoting to a collaborative perspective, a shift born out of reflection so that no blood need be spilt in order to change society. It would also be a start to alleviating the anxiety ridden mess this country has become. Moreover, fighting and constantly competing is dull, and boring."

"Now who sounds like a child?"

"I'm just being playful about it." Peach lowered himself off the end of the wall and waited for Thomas, who took the stairs. "An example. What if we took the game of scrabble, and just played it in a slightly different way? To lay out all of one's tiles, still forming words, still following most of the game's directions, till there's a board full of words that everyone has contributed to. Instead of ending here, with the winner and losers decided, the players then create a story out of the jumble of words on the board. Perhaps the individual with the most points might decide the theme of the story, or the person with the most points has only the responsibility of entering the stories created into the house book of scrabble."

"Or why not create a new game, with its own set of rules?"

"Because I don't think we *need* any more *stuff* to be made. All that is required for metamorphosis and a shift in perspective is already here. There are giant floating islands of plastic in the oceans, why create more? Humboldt, some two hundred years ago, decried the infamous deforestation in South America, yet still it continues."

"So why would you think you can change that now?"

"By introducing a creative aspect, the feeling of being excluded because of your class or intelligence level that can be attached to this game of words at present, is diminished. If everyone has access to the shared vocabulary, to the creative act, in order to build something together, playing becomes an exercise in collaboration. If you can introduce this idea to scrabble, there is the potential for opening up other parts of society too. Also, if the dissatisfaction is felt together then at the same time as pissing more people off, there also are more people to help."

"But then, they're still standing against something."

"Not once they've started. Once they start creating, something entirely unbelievable can happen. Repetition becomes less engrained, perhaps it becomes impossible - wouldn't that be a marvellous thing?"

They stopped a moment outside the Lifeboat station. A middle-age woman, wrapped in a tan tartan shawl, on a mobility scooter rolled past them as they sat on a bench. Indifferent to the potholes on the pavement, she drove onto the start of Victoria crescent and took to the road. The Queen's Head pub stood empty, nubs of cigarette ash darted about beneath the benches and a gull stood on the doorstep calling down the morning.

"And what about the people who don't want to play? The people who feel uncomfortable about it or mistrustful or attacked?"

"By a board game?"

They stood up and carried on walking.

"Well, with that much weight behind it, wouldn't you be a bit timid?"

"Not me,"

"But you're a nut, not everyone thinks like you."

"And I'm not asking them to, I want them to think for themselves."

The pair walked in their own thoughts along the curve of the terraces. Thomas kept his eyes on the paving slabs, a habit he had picked up from assisting the residents in wheelchairs. He clenched and opened his fists to move some blood into them, the chill of the sea wind got under his collar. He had walked this road before. During the previous summer, on one of the fourteen-hour shifts, he had taken this way between Tynemouth and Whitley Bay with one of the residents. It got them both out and away from the confines of the care home but also away from the glares and condescension of the other staff. Thomas had helped pushing his wheelchair, and all fifteen stone of him, along the three miles between Tynemouth Metro and the seafront.

Thomas kicked at the tufts of grass coming up between some of the slabs and returned from his thoughts.

"But what about the six-year-olds who attack teachers now? And the 'stick-your-kid-in front-of-computer-games' logic? What happens to that?"

"It has to be shown to be unnecessary and unhealthy, and for…"

"But what about the people who don't have time, because of low wage jobs or bad experiences of their own or a disillusionment with 'the system'?"

"The concept has to wax at a cultural level – and involve children. Children are the best teachers of change and collaboration, I think."

"You're saying that children with the opportunity to create something can and will?"

"Yes, without a doubt."

They came onto the Promenade. The fisherman's stoops were empty – but, by night the loners and young grandfathers, the milkmen and the deliverymen perched here and cast out lines into the night; hoping for something to bite. There was a stark contrast between the pavement and the modern grey street slabs that looked like lost teeth. Many of the house fronts were unlit. The old business sites were empty. Lots stood vacant, surrounded by builders' railings that were bent and burnt and left to rust. The Rex Hotel and Deep bar on the corner had been abandoned for years. Windows kicked out, doors panelled over with chipboard and graffiti. The threats of legal action for trespassing hung everywhere. The stains of disregard left after the boom of stag parties and boozy weekends waned. All left for the taking.

"Then why are our schools in crisis?"

"Well, if the curriculum is monitored and ordained within the logic of the ruling cultural ideas, its function will be to keep that status quo in place. Authority, competition, a rigid curriculum, key performance indicators. Factor in austerity, and you've crushed any hope of nurturing the creative spirit. Not to mention, what lies ahead for young people, at the moment, is not such a great set of options either."

"Not really, is it? My sister is a teacher and she has to struggle to get through with the resources they've got. On top of that she has to teach the kids manners and how to interact socially with others, but it's not her responsibility alone. Does she really have to explain to a seven-year-old why it's wrong to attack someone with a fire extinguisher?"

"No, but why do some parents assume that she should have to? The deeper and deeper we get into a culture of not taking responsibility for our actions the wider and wider the impact becomes. If the sole function of politics, as was clearly stated a decade ago or there abouts, was for the economy, how can you expect that anything fruitful for society or education will be born? And if people can't or don't take responsibility for their actions, places like Blackpool end up like a third-world city on this island. Then what point is there in saying 'well, let's just cut ourselves off more?' The people voted to leave Europe and yet there is little movement to revitalise local industry, or people taking the initiative to build up..."

"But, they can't because there's no funding..."

"But the money and the resources are all already on the island. It is a matter of shifting vast sums of static wealth, into clear areas of need. But I'm getting off topic for now – I'm supposed to be talking about games."

"No matter how much wealth, there is a lack of something intimate that leads people such a way, to hold onto something and not share."

"Perhaps even that lady at the care home was once just a child," said Peach.

Thomas cringed, trying to ignore the last comment. They walked down the path to the beach and towards the Rendezvous café. Thomas took off his shoes too and idled along beside Peach, stopping sometimes to pick up shards of sea glass. Peach ruminated on the last remark and kept to himself. A couple of times he reached for his tobacco pouch, but left it in his pocket. The sea rolled in and about the feet of children who stood near their parents at the shore's edge. Up soared a screamed mixture of joy and surprise each time the water swallowed their toes and ankles. A young man in a grey tracksuit held the reins of a kite shaped like a dragon. He jerked on the line, making the kite shudder and bop on the current. The lady stood next to him put a pen and notepad back in her pocket and joined in.

Peach and Thomas got nearer to the Rendezvous café, but chose a place to sit on the beach instead of going inside. They stayed in silence for a time. The roll of the waves pushed and pulled the sand around the bay before them. Thomas dug his toes underneath the rocks and grains. Peach squinted at the offshore wind turbines. Often, when he got tired or distracted, he would look for a way to control the situation or conversation. Even without meaning to. Though it didn't usually go as he imagined. But he had learnt how to keep this behaviour in check. When he felt himself failing to get his own way, he would confront the need to take over and his usual self would be roused from under the desire to dominate. However, the whole process leant his face a dour expression and could make him become irritable and morose.

"Games?" Asked Thomas, trying to get him to carry on.

"The suitcase story game," he said quietly, almost to himself.

"The what? Mate, just because it's in your head doesn't mean it's in mine," replied Thomas with a sharpness in his tone.

"Allow me to get to it," he picked up, "one person, say an adult or parent at a children's birthday party, or in a classroom, or on a weekend, or whenever, fills a suitcase full of objects. The children choose a character, a start point, a destination and perhaps one key event that happens along the way. The suitcase is then opened, whereby each child is allowed to choose one object at a time. They are asked to sit with the object, think about what it is, what it's called, get them to describe it, get them to think about how it can be used in the story. Children's imaginations have fewer fixed filters and cultural reference points. Thus, with the facilitator steering them towards using their own ideas, instead of repeating the ones say from television or books or computer games, they learn how to take what they know, but use it in a different way, for a different purpose, whilst gaining a deeper connection with material objects that they may encounter in the culture as they grow older. It may also reach places you or I could never imagine. The children may tell us a story we could never otherwise believe, if we had not witnessed it being created."

"But, what about the parents who don't have a suitcase, let alone any *things* to put in it?"

"Well then, there is a game that needs no *thing*. It is called 'Three words and a name'. You can play it alone, but it's infinitely more fun with two or more. The listener gives three words and a name to the one chosen to create a story. The storyteller can make up any kind of story, they can let the world around them influence them. It could be a sentence long, or it could go on for hours. The only rule the storyteller has to follow is that they must use the three words and the name in the story. The listener gets to listen, but has to keep attentive and keep an ear out for the words and the name. Then the roles get switched."

"But, what about the parents and children who aren't so confident playing those kinds of games?"

"I'm optimistic. I trust in people. And, as the social environment changes, the fear of participating, of losing, would be irrelevant. Human nature is too adaptable to be purely competitive! To be stuck in a fight with minimal outcomes. Fuck Hobbes and Locke and all the harm they have done to a future they could never imagine!

"Peach! Calm down. Do you really think it's realistic to change peoples' approach to the world around them with just games?"

"Now you're being defeatist. That's cynicism and apathy! That's not you saying or thinking that! You know full well more than this struggle is possible, and not in some profound glorified Disney sense!"

"I'm not being apathetic!"

"You are! You're not even entertaining the idea that someone different to yourself could sit down and play a game with their children. Besides, people don't need my hope, they need their own!"

"Peach, you're infuriating."

"But, I'm right! The hope is that they will have a deeper connection with the material world so that they may one day refuse to accept that objects are without value, in a cold horrible universe and instead start with the idea that one object can serve many purposes and that gives it value beyond anything money could ever account for."

"Like that circle - the one you turn sideways to reveal it's a spiral" quipped Thomas.

"Yes mate, and that is a skill that has to be nurtured and it, hopefully, will open up the imagination of children to see how all objects can be used in a way that eliminates waste and want for more than we have or need."

"You're oversimplifying. That's reducing – that's just being thrifty!"

"Is it? Then you're looking at it from a different point of view than me. From my stance it involves collaboration and curiosity. Perspective is the key, the lens, the focus, whatever name you want to give it. That is the key to it all! Not deluded positive thinking, not Hare Krishna bells or the Popes hat, not Kerouac's craic, or a fascists knuckle. Making the commonplace significant is integral to grasping the paradox of the cultural logic we live within."

"For fuck's sake!"

Thomas pushed the heels of his hands deeper into the sand. He felt the wet grains sticking to his palms. A gust of wind caught his face and he began to cry. His shoulders rocked toward the sea and his head fell forward.

"I can't hear this mate, what about that lady from the job, eh? How's that ever going to change? You know what she did to me when we went to Blackpool?" He turned to Peach. "I sat in the back of the minibus, all the way to fucking Blackpool. Almost three hours! And all she did was spend the drive digging and digging into me, telling me all the things she couldn't stand about me, whilst fucking matey boy just drove and listened. It was horrible, but you know what? Somewhere around the outskirts of elsewhere, I don't, I don't know where on the way, but there was forest all around and my eyes closed while she was rattling on and I felt this massive warp of electricity wrap around my head and my eyes, like one of them plasma globes. And all I could see around me was black, and I was inside an old diving marionette, descending, deeper and deeper into this blackness and I couldn't hear her anymore, but I could feel all of this electrical power and current connecting me to the other people in the minibus, even to her, and to the windows and through the windows and into the trees and I was in the branches and the wind and in the soil and I was descending, not falling, but sinking, only I didn't feel scared, or strange or worried, but just going deeper into it." Thomas curled his fingers around the sand and brought it up in his fists and squeezed. "And do you know where I ended up?"

149

"No, where mate?" Peach had fallen silent. In his patience he had leaned back onto his elbow and held himself open towards Thomas.

"I ended up on a cliff, under glorious sunshine, sat beneath a lone juniper tree; overlooking a bay. There, beside the tree was me, and this lady and a fuck off giant bucket of salt. And we sat in silence, pinching the salt and throwing it back into the sea." He breathed in deep and exhaled slowly. "Then, when the bucket was empty, I put it next to the tree then threw her off the cliff, just the same as the salt. Without violence, not murder, but the end of the stress she had caused me, putting it back into the chaos of the water below. It felt safe to throw her, I knew it wouldn't bring her any harm. And then I started floating back up in the darkness. All the while we'd been travelling further and when I opened my eyes, she'd stopped having a dig at me, and he was still driving and the residents were all sat about watching the world inside and outside the minibus go by. And."

"And?" Said Peach, sitting up.

"And it felt ok. Somehow, I turned all her vitriol into a calm I hadn't known for years."

"And wasn't that around the time you stopped drinking?"

Thomas stopped squeezing the sand. The tension went out of his shoulders and they dropped a little. He unclenched his fists and let the sand fall, slowly from his fingers; before putting his hands, palm down, on to the beach.

"Fuck."

"Imagine, if you didn't have to find ways to do it only with peoples' negative energy. If she is the sum of her experiences under the harsh wages of old ideas and lobbyists then, when the rules of competitive culture are changed, the possibilities for the future, and for people are, theoretically and potentially limitless - even for her" said Peach.

"That's the most unpoetic way of saying that! William Blake would be so upset with you."

He faced the sea and watched the tide carrying the white tops of the waves onto the beach.

"Yeah, and the last time I was skint I started washing windows and doors for a living. Why don't you go for a swim mate?"

Thomas pursed his lips, nodding slowly. The light from the afternoon cast him like a silhouette from where Peach sat. He lurched backwards then, with a hand on Peach's shoulder, pulled himself up and pushed his mate down. He looked about and saw dog walkers far off, the lady with the pram shuffling across the shoreline towards St Mary's lighthouse; a mess of teenagers down towards Spanish city. He pulled off his clothes and walked to the water naked. He didn't shout at the water's edge, he let the cold come to him. He waded out further until he was knee deep in the North Sea. Peach watched on in silence. Thomas reached the shelf of the land and dove into a wave; disappearing beneath the horizon.

Chapter 7. No mistakes. No miracles. Building trust.

The doors closed behind them on the South Shields line of the Metro. The carriage was half full, most people were either chatting into mobile phones or jabbing at them. Anytime one of them rang, most people looked about themselves; a strange conditioned consequence. Thomas stared at the sea before it fell away, out of sight behind the houses. The line of the Metro curved inland, past Monkseaton and through the last remaining land before the building sites and the housing estates swallowed it up between Shiremoor and Northumberland Park.

Peach stretched out his fingers, then let them curl up into fists. After the doors closed at Four Lanes End, Thomas heard him humming, quietly; just beneath the chatter and shout in the carriage. Peach rested his hands on his thighs and drummed his fingers, pushing into his legs like he would the keys of a piano.

"What are you humming mate?"

"Lilac Iris."

"How come?"

"I'm thinking. Letting our chat about games mull over a bit. If I hum it, I feel more concentrated on my thoughts. Kind of like how it is for some people with their headphones, only I make my own music; not listen to someone else's. If I am the one making the noise, I feel more engaged than passive."

Thomas nodded, leaving Peach to carry on entertaining himself and his thoughts. He finished humming at South Gosforth and closed his eyes for a moment. Thomas felt the rise and fall of Peach's shoulder on his own as he breathed. Out of the corner of his eye he watched his friends' head slowly sagged froward. In the moment his chin touched his chest he erupted in a peculiar spasm, yelling and shaking his hands as if he had been electrocuted. Thomas looked out the window at the trees, waiting for Peach to settle down.

"So, what's your new thoughts then?" Asked Thomas.

Peach rubbed his face. He stared at Thomas with a blank expression for a moment, then closed his eyes again, reached into his coat pocket and pulled out the tincture bottle of eucalyptus oil. With both eyes still shut, he unscrewed the cap and put it up to his nose; drawing a measure of the essence up each nostril. As he breathed out, he opened his eyes again; his gaze more in focus.

"So, what's new then?" Repeated Thomas.

"Well," Peach began, pulling a satsuma from another pocket as he dropped the bottle back inside his coat. He fished out another orange and offered to Thomas, who accepted. "I think, that there is also an affirmation of confidence that is a consequence of game playing and this really valuable for a child. The focus required to play a game encourages an individual to engage with it, to enter an active period of reflection, in which there is the possibility to learn skills for reflection on the days or most recent events. The need for reflection is so vital now, at this point in our culture's existence, I'd hasten to recommend, as I do already, for everyone to read the poem *One Almost Might* by A.S.J. Tessimond and another poem, by Raymond Carver called *At Least*. Both engage with the need to reflect and to be able to draw one's own conclusions."

"But why would people listen? It sounds too close to the stereotype of 'too-much-introspection' groups."

"It might sound similar, but it has to be taken very serious because it is for all, not just exclusively for one group who believe themselves enlightened and entitled. If only the wealthy can afford the time to reflect or to live sustainably then what the fuck chance have you or I got? You couldn't even afford to pay for the recycling bins after the council 'recalled' them and charged people for them."

"Fuck, I need to remember to talk to the house about that."

"How many things do we have to remember? One can also consider two grounding ideas: that to make mistakes and accept them is to learn through one's own experience, this is widely popular in the rhetoric about being a genius – though it applies to everyone, genius or not – and the other is that failure is not possible. If there is only one victor or an external thought process determining your perspective then one will not want to make their own mistakes for fear of shame or embarrassment, both of which can be causes of anxiety. Equally, the knowledge that failure is impossible will not be learnt in a tangible way, it will remain only an empty phrase, a slogan. It's impossible to fail if you collaborate with others. You may not have the answer, but someone else may have an idea; why not listen?"

"You sound a bit like you're expecting miracles from some people."

The Metro pulled out of the darkness and stopped at the platform of Central station. They stepped off in the middle of the crowd and made their way to the ticket barriers.

"Ha! No because I'm not looking for miracles, and a miracle is what? Perhaps, just finding a way to act, or conceive of a thing, that doesn't make sense in that point in history? I'm waiting for humans to arrive at their own decision to, oddly enough, want more from life. That's why some of the adverts are so confusing! Want more from life sounds like an aspirational campaign for selling over the counter Viagra or diet pills, or fruit flavoured water! How bizarre! That's how easy it is to be distracted; all these words get defined in connection to the products they sell. What about a process of redefinition? Of a national Epic Poem where we can redefine all the words to have meaning without spurious connections to consumer goods or the merchant economy?"

"You mean, nurturing myself instead of investing time on myself?"

"Fuck yes!" Peach roared.

They stepped through the turnstiles. Both of them went to the ticket machines, up onto their tiptoes and left their tickets on top of the machines before walking up the stairs to the Neville street entrance. They emerged into dusk and to a soft, ash blue light that coloured the hotels and bars opposite the station and the buses destined for West Denton Park, North Walbottle, Chapel House. The taxi drivers swore as they were spurned by the early-evening drunks. The garret tower of the Mining Institute lit up from inside and a man appeared at the window. On the steps of the Lit and Phil library a violinist tuned up before heading inside to play a concert. The throng of people danced into the streets undressing the stress of the day, the week, the winter, as they filled the pubs, or shrieked at passing cars, or wend their way elsewhere.

"Peach, you're shining again"

"Ha, but it'd be great! To make a new dictionary! Why not? I mean our turns of phrase need an overhaul, like the corruption of one of our languages most important, emotional, questions: *how are you?* That this question has become synonymous with a throwaway hello scares me a little. First time I really

158

thought about it was when I moved to live in Canada. I went to a public lecture on Canadian culture, thinking that I didn't need to be there because it already felt so similar to British culture, but I was wrong. The speaker told the room that 'the question, *how are you?* Doesn't really require an answer. The other person is using it only as a greeting.' If that is the case, and I have discussed this with many people, why do we persist in using it as a brief greeting?"

"Because it's a polite transaction that allows us to slowly build a connection, to build intimacy with someone else. It's like bum-sniffing for dogs, friend or foe or partner."

They walked to the front doors of the station. Peach peered inside, pulled the lapels of his coat down and sniffed at the young man playing at the piano. Not unkindly, more inquisitive and instinctive. He returned, stretched out his arms and, flexing down the fingers, held his wrists up to the sky.

"I understand that, but why not ask it a different way? 'What's occurring?' for example, starts even slower, and people are more likely to listen, sincerely, to that answer than being prepared to listen to how someone is emotionally."

"People do listen, Peach!"

"Mate, whenever I answered that question, I got told off for being intense and too much for people! And I asked them to ask a different question, that's all! Surely, we need only ask it if we want to know how that person is feeling? Not just another routine transaction. If you want form a bond with me, ask a different question, try something else. I believe it is an abuse of language that supports our emotionally dysfunctional attitude towards ourselves and to other people. If we learn to deflect the answer about how someone is, do we thus expect other people to not really care about how we are, do we further learn how to reduce our emotional connection to one another through three words? Isn't that scary?"

The first of the evenings marital parties fled the station, a gang of women dressed up as Vikings; a group of men in garish dresses and wigs.

"It's also about trust Peach. And you do have a tendency to not shut up, once you start."

"I'm exuberant is all, and today sober! All of this life in me without alcohol!" he turned aside and muttered to himself

160

"perhaps, I don't need to wait for St Lucy's" he squeezed his thumbs to his forefingers, spat on the ground and stamped his right foot. Peach looked at Thomas, who nodded and a subtle smile curled up the left side of his mouth. "And I trust people!" he continued, "But that's another difference between competition and collaboration."

"How?"

"If we have to be suspicious of one another then it requires us to build a trust contract with one another. If we already consent to collaboration, on a cultural level, we form trust in a different way."

Peach stepped aside, but pulled his lighter from his pocket. He held it out to no one Thomas could see until, out of the doors, emerged a young lady patting down her pockets. She looked up and saw Peach holding it out towards her. She cocked a smile and took the lighter.

"But that would freak people out Peach, no wonder people think you're intense! Why would everyone trust you?" Peach smiled back and told her to keep the lighter. She walked towards the Centre for life and he looked at Thomas.

"It doesn't have to be me who they trust, they have to trust themselves."

"No mate, it involves trusting others. That is part of your project with games, that requires trust."

"The starting point must be trusting yourself, knowing the world for you. If you don't know or decide your world view for yourself then you'll have only this vague, delusional or coerced trust in an 'other'. If that's where you're at, then you have come to experience trust as just an image of trust; not much more than a trick or a confidence game. It will leave you feeling insecure, even when you believe you shouldn't. It'll give you the dread that breads denial. And what does that give you? The freedom to live in the likeness of trust, but not in a trusting relationship to yourself and other people? Is that the way you'd want to live?"

"No," replied Thomas, after a moments consideration, "if every relationship is only the imitation of the real then where is the value? If we live in a way we cannot really claim to value, then surely that will lead to a kind of depression?"

The young man who'd been sat at the piano stood up and left to catch his train. There was no one else in the wings by the barrier so Peach stepped inside and beckoned Thomas to follow, rolling his fingers. He sat down, pushed his hands against the chest of the piano and breathed in. Thomas squatted down beside him, his back against the glass that protected the masonry. The sounds of the people peeled off the walls and the high-vaulted ceiling; the announcements echoed and ricocheted across their heads; the clatter of change dropped at a ticket machines; the laughter of a woman filled the station ante-chamber.

"Yes. And this practice of likening reality to itself is deep rooted in our culture. In all kinds of places. It's the same reason I detest American sitcoms that started the excessive use of the word 'like'," said Peach without looking up. "That it became a normal addition to a sentence so quickly alarmed me, think about it: the word 'like' is an adjective that means to bear resemblance. If people have learnt to experience the culture around them as only the semblance of the culture around them is this not fearfully alienating? It makes everything into a fiction. Two humans walk out of a copse towards a noise they can hear. They find a body of water that they can find neither

163

source nor end. One says 'Ah, it's a river'." Peached dropped his forefinger onto the middle E.

"The other says 'Ah, it's, like, a river.'" He formed an E minor chord and embellished it with an A and A sharp.

"Both have agreed that it is a river, but the first has used the language to engage with the river more directly. The second is engaging with the river as if it is a semblance of itself. Some may even just go swimming. But I noticed it getting worse around the same time British television started showing High School Musical. Around the same time some people started calling a secondary state school a 'High School'. But I digress."

He began with a sort of Balkan Ska in E minor to make himself smile.

"To return to the two approaches to mistakes and failure, if one doesn't learn from their actions, one runs the risk of repeating the logic that led to the mistake and – although possibly getting a different version of the same consequence – continuing the infinite revolution that the DSM defines as insane. To repeat the same action and believe it will work out differently next time is insane; the capacity for variation, alteration, divergence is what separates us from insanity."

"That's also the logic that makes sitcoms," Thomas joined in, watching Peach's wrists as they arched and strained at the ends of his cuffs, "incorrigible characters making the same, endless mistakes. Nothing ever changing, variations on the same malady. That used to upset me so much, when they would put the telly on at the residence and watch the same shite every evening. The only thing that would change between the shows was the setting, in a London street, in Manchester, in the countryside. No wonder our parents can no longer see past the personalities that now run the government. If you see every night, more of the same and no change."

Peach increased the pace of the piece he was playing. He stared up towards the roof and bellowed '*Shaskabiti*'. He once fell in love with a version of *Kalinka* that an English folk band used to play. He had created this piece by accident, whilst trying to learn it.

"This constant repetition and insanity as the norm, can be observed in our cultures history and more widely in a global history as well. This is where, sadly, the use of manipulation and fashion plays a part. When our culture is faced with the imminence of the realisation that it is insane, the fashion changes. That which is 'popular' is used to ignore the root that we are living in an insane culture. All to maintain a status quo."

He broke off from the piano, his hands suspended in front of him, and looked at Thomas.

"That same nuance is observable in these deluded hipster renegades who believe urban hydroponic farming is the future. That is *a solution* to a sore, a running wound, a symptom; not the root problem that we have become incapable of sustaining ourselves and thus require technological intervention. Technology, although useful for somethings, is not the solution to everything. In the state of exhaustion, the easiest option is to get something or someone else to do the work and at a faster rate than you can do it."

Peach paused and stretched out his wrists.

"But even in this reliance on technology there is the seed of our collaborative nature. We are adaptors. We are resourceful and co-operative. And my fear is, if people are not capable of

166

rest and reflection, then a project such as hydroponic farming can become popular – even for a brief while – and the people who believe they are the creators of an alternative future are in fact the progenitors of their own future enslavement and torture by stealing the fertility of the land and doing nothing to replenish it."

"You mean, instead of making farming more ecologically friendly, hydroponics gives farming a frame that is more in line with the idea of manufacturing?" asked Thomas.

"Yes, mate."

Peach's left hand started moving again, the middle three fingers began plying the bass end F major notes.

"Look at the arguments for hydroponic farming as 'the future of farming and food production'. Sustenance cannot be a middle-class fashionable protest; it is far too important and serious for that. On the grounds that the soil is no longer sufficient to provide for the ever-growing population, we are presented with the idea for urban, hydroponic farming; increased manipulation of light and water cycles to speed up food production in order to feed the masses. Most of the seeds are genetically modified to tolerate such intensive farming and can create an abundance of fruit or veg in a relatively small amount of space. My concern is that it becomes fashionable; enough people throw money behind the idea and it claims the tagline, copyrighting 'the future of farming' and thus gaining a legal hold on the power to define farming. But it is dangerous; it addresses only the symptom of the problem of food resources. There are enough people working on ethical, sustainable crop rotation patterns, biodynamic agriculture and on ways to rest and reinvigorate soil to maintain its fertility, without chemical synthesis, but these have become marginalised practices and why? In some instances, it's because of the 'lone wolf' attitude of living off the grid creates exclusive communities, but also because real farming is hard work, demands our time, requires commitment, something we are losing the grasp of as a result of a prevalence and tendency to instant gratification. Whether the perseverance with agriculture has done us any good is also up for debate. But to accept we've been ruining our resources, accepting we got it wrong and taking a step back to try again, in a different way, would be damaging to the ego or pride, or simply unrealistic in some peoples' logic because of the scale of demand for the food. But fuck, I'd love to be wrong about that."

He coughed and found a dead note on the keyboard with his right hand. He tinkered with it, as he continued playing with his left hand, until something inside fell back into place.

"Especially," Peach continued, "if the alternative means forging ahead with an idea that could endanger the livelihood of economies that depend upon the harvest and seasonal labour to feed their families. In some country's governments are under the thumb of the IMF and trade agreements, like Jamaica, who fought for decades to produce their own goods to export instead of being mere subsidiaries of larger economies. There is a great potential for learning that occurs in the solitude of farming. We run the risk of destroying ecosystems, life, livelihoods and the varieties of nourishment that create pleasure, knowledge and culture, true peculiar culture; not just a bastard copy of the elsewhere shite that clogs up so many minds."

He faced the piano again, adding trills and flourishes with his right hand across the higher octaves. Thomas noticed a young man walking in the front door of the station. In one hand he held a laptop case and in the other a carrier bag. He looked about and, noticing the person he was coming to meet, pretended to hide. A lady came over to him and gave him a gentle shove. He put down the laptop case and kissed her on the cheek as he stood up again. From the bag he pulled a box of pasta and a jar of pesto. She laughed at him and lent down, picking up his other bag. She pulled him out of the door and towards the city buses.

"I wonder how Mary is," Thomas whispered to himself, drifting off into the dusty palaces of human memory. He looked back towards Peach who had returned to playing with just his left hand.

"Look at Northern Italy for example," Peach said, his tone rising and filling up with reverence, "the vegetables they produce are still celebrated in festivals. Asparagus, fucking asparagus has its own window in the calendar in some regions, harvested and prepared, served in giant terracotta urns full of goat cheese; to be celebrated for its flavour and richness in the company of family, friends, strangers, along century old tables. A single vegetable, but if we chose hydroponic farming as 'a future', what would happen then? People, the exclusive crème of hip culture, would they go raving in the LED tunnels with the *enhanced* lentils grown in upcycled troughs, next to uniform rows of vegetables without sun ripened flavours? Fuck that. 'Oh, get on with it, this is the future'. My skin! It is only 'a future', not 'the future' it is only one idea and the sooner our culture is more open and less a venture of vested, moneyed interest, or fixed on this *overcoming nature* mantra of the technological fix, the more creative it can become. And what happens to all these new enterprises when circumstance or *karma* turns off the energy source? They all need to be plugged in or have a store of electricity, same with new currency arguments for block chain transparency. Great idea, but what happens when the energy source isn't there?"

An announcement for the delayed London bound train boomed around the entry hall.

"But mate," interrupted Thomas, "I don't think that the source of energy is really a problem. I mean the technology is there. It's reliable and sustainable."

"Yes, but that is relying on an assumption, that the energy source will always be there. But the way in which these sustainable energy sources are made. Are they sustainable? What if the minerals needed to make the computer components come from mines that operate with less than humane ethics? Assumptions blind us to that. And we rely on assumptions when we're tired. I'm not speaking in hour or

171

weeks here. I mean in centuries time span. And how many solutions or options are being created at present that are the fantastical result of a cultured mind that is exhausted or resting on assumptions? It's like dreaming of automated sofas to carry you home. These techno-opportunists are the grand, contemporary example of the prisoner who has learnt to love his shackles. The hippies in the 'Golden Era' were much the same and it is that 'baby boomer' generation, that really dove into these future technologies, that we are now cleaning up after."

"And, grand Peach, how would you propose we do that? But before you carry on, can you accept that some technology is valuable," retorted Thomas.

"Mate, I'm not decrying all technology. It provides an abundance of situations that would never have before existed. I'm decrying the consequence that people have become accustomed to shirking off their responsibility, waiting for the next techno-*miracle* to replace the need to contend with a very practical problem. Jumping on some technological fix does not engage with the root problem. If we could take a deep breath and some time to consider the problem with humility then we would see that technology will of course play a part in the response to a situation, we are a tool-wielding species after all, but tech is not the entire response!"

He stopped rolling his left hand over the bass end notes. The dorsum of both his hands were pale and streaked with violet veins. He bunched his fingers together, trying to make them warm. He turned his head to either side, breathing through his nose like a horse.

"In the example of food production," continued Peach, "As I said, technology is a part of 'a future' not 'the future', this island and the way we understand it, and our options, cannot be drawn into the extremities of neo-religious fervour or the historical context of utopias and dystopias; it's far more hopeful than that."

The bile subsided and he settled into a lazy piece in F major, without a time signature.

"Hold in mind sunshine," Peach continued, "this is not an act of *attack* towards my parents' generation. They made their action as a rebellion against their parents' generation and has gone wildly out of proportion. They were lied to about plastics. They were raised by anxious, controlling parents;

themselves traumatised by the violence of wars. They saw the need for interconnectivity, but let individuals decide how to do this instead of deciding with people. They applied a singular way of thinking to solve a problem that is unique to every place it occurs. And this has backfired horribly.

"So it means that one aspect of this transition to a collaborative, communal perspective would be the need to continue helping and encouraging the 'baby boomer' generation to become capable of reflection. To enable them to accept the need to relinquish their roles as leaders of a culture that has done harm and caused a great deal of imbalance. The state of the planet testifies to a need to change. But simply carrying on a screaming match with them isn't going to help. You and I have inherited an encyclopaedia of trauma and deceit and the consequences of a *competitive nature*, but they are not to blame in the traditional sense. They have inherited it from their family and back and back for generations. They must step down, apologise and adapt to life beyond the ken of a dying thought process. And it is part of our generation to aid that transition. For this generation and whoever comes next it must be there to see; that we can change. That is a start. Only a start mind and only one part of a much bigger project. But it is enough, no seeking of violence, no aggression, start with

174

sincere concern for them as wanton idealists who have burnt out, much as a child grows petulant when it hasn't learnt the capacity to decide when it needs to sleep, because it doesn't yet know what to 'going to sleep' is yet. The same goes for denying death, or wanting to overcome nature. If we don't respond to this lack of awareness, how will we ever stop fighting an impossible war on their terms?"

"And if we were to find a way of appealing to the needs of people, on a more elemental level and in their own language," Thomas added, "it could be possible to draw the attention of a people once wrapped up in competition towards a collaborative perspective; in ways that all of us can understand."

Thomas stood up and, knowing the piece, joined in with a D minor accompaniment that Peach had showed him how to play. Thomas had dreamed of playing the piano, ever since he was a child, but it wasn't until Peach taught himself that Thomas got to learn through and from him. Most often the lessons were in exchange for a place to sleep as Peach could, invariably, find a keyboard to borrow or a piano nearby.

"Yes, mate. That's why our stories and music is a great starting place. Besides, they had some interesting ideas," Peach continued, "or at least the beginning of some interesting ideas, but it takes time for ideas to mature and develop, beyond the ken of rebellion against. Mate, I always wonder if the word rebel could be an active word. To 'rebel with', to 'rebel for'. It's such a lovely little word that still contains so much potential."

Thomas felt his blood changing, electrifying; flushed with the relief that comes as the soul opens up when we join in with other people, or play music with someone else.

"It is also a perfect point, in the context of our culture," Peach began, "to encourage a reframing of competitive practice because many of us are starting to realise the degree to which we depend on one another. In one aspect, the population is living longer and thankfully we are better understanding of people with different needs, or means to communicate; or ways to live than our own. In order to function, in some coherent way, we require acts of cooperation and collaboration. These acts already exist! The joy with which I recount this to you is caused by the fact that all of these things and what will follow already exists in the world. It's all already there, it just needs looking at a little differently; it needs calling by a different name perhaps."

The piece moved into a melancholic A minor seam and Thomas stepped away, leaving Peach with full run of the keys. He lent on the glass wall between him and the masonry. He tucked his hands inside his jacket. The café on the other side of the entry was closing for the evening. The barista waved him over and offered him two pastries left over from the day. He bit into the apricot filled croissant and put the other on the pianos' shoulder. He put a hand into Peach's coat and fished about for some spare change. He found a couple coins and pulled off Peach's hat, putting the coins in and placing it on the floor beside him as he played.

"'Why not?' Is the logical question of this generation rather than 'why'?" He carried on, undisturbed by Thomas going through his pockets. "In the same moment it can be encouraging and elicit considerate advice. It seeks explanations using reason and experience, rather than putting someone on the defensive. It is not cavalier; it is well considered. And can help locate a persons' anxieties or learnt opinions and challenge them. And instead of further giving up our control, over the risks involved in our daily lives, to outside organisations, –

organisations that advertise they operate 'in our best interests', although we know they do not,- what about walking back into ourselves, accepting the need to say we are wrong and that we want help and we want to help others?"

"Breathe Peach, your chewing brain here!"

Someone dropped a pound into the hat. Someone dropped a penny. Peach transitioned back to the F major and slowed down, before stopping to rest.

"You're right, I'll slow down a bit. I just get excited. It's also important to challenge the belief that controlling a person or situation is acceptable. Especially now. The sensation of being put on the defensive, to be in a position of inferiority is dangerous. It leads to all kinds of violence. And what is control? A consequence of this either, or thinking? A consequence of needing to be right? An old grudge?"

He stretched out his hands. His were not perfect fingers. Some of the knuckles were bent, the veins bulged on the dorsum and the nails were always dirty with rind or the grit of frankincense. Both hands were scarred many times over in odd shapes. But they were his. With his right thumb and little finger, he teased the high-end G octave and rattled up the scale with his left hand in a ragtime fashion.

"Control is debilitating, that's for sure," added Thomas.

"True. And if you're a child now, who is growing up with technology, it is highly likely, through the nigh constant updates and creation of new devices, that their parents lack the understanding and knowledge about how to use these things and what to do with them. This leads to constant probing and the need for explanation is high. Explanations that the parents simply don't have. And so, too grows the inability to control the things and people we engage with; even the one's we consider family."

"Yeah, but you're not a parent so how can you presume," replied Thomas.

"Mate, if you are anywhere outside in public these days you become a witness to the spectacle. It comes from talking to other people, parents. I mean look at yourself. We're of the generation that had all these phones and hand-held devices as we were becoming teenagers. It was scary and exciting, but the pace of change for these devices now is alarming."

A pair of children and their mother stopped to listen. The children stood behind her legs. They held onto her coat as they watched Peach bouncing on the piano stool, his arms pumping furiously at the keys. Slowly, they let go of their mothers' coat, stepped forward and started dancing like wild humans.

"There are more, and more reports," he shouted over the roar of the piano, "about kids trying to swipe their hands over books." Peach caught sight of himself in the glass wall and adjusted the pace of his playing to continue the conversation. "And having to understand how to raise a child with or without the knowledge of how to use these devices must be scary as well."

"It is comparable to when people first sat children in front of televisions. Different, but similar."

"True, different but similar. It is also another skill people are forced to acquire, in most cases without a teacher. Really, how would you feel if you had to ask a 'genius' to explain to you how to fix your phone? That's the backfoot again. And some people would never go into the phone shop, they just struggle on until aggression rears up and there's a kind of confrontation, or a projection of this frustration. Is this perhaps why some

180

children are becoming more aggressive or living in more aggressive households?"

"Mate, that's a jump. It could be *a* factor."

"I didn't say it was the only factor."

He turned his attention back to the piano and changed the rhythm, making it jumpier and jaunty. The kids ran in circles, looping through each other's trajectory like wild spinning tops. He rolled through scales up and down the piano, his arms sawing away; much to the amusement of the children. Their mother dropped a fiver before whispering thank you in his ear and, collecting her son and daughter, left the station.

"It adds to the confusion of not knowing what we really want or need," Peach added as he slowed his breathing. "Most of the time it reminds me of that comedy sketch about wanting to eat a biscuit and having so many choices it ends in doom and fear."

"Yeah, but that's funny."

"Yes, but it's overwhelming and if people can't figure that out, how are they expected to make decisions about other situations? Many times, in films and comedy have we seen this becoming a joke. But accepting and laughing at it alone doesn't alter the reality that there will still be a ridiculous amount of biscuits."

On the other side of the piano appeared a middle-aged man, his shoulders wrapped in a sleeping bag; his free hand held up his three pairs of trackie bottoms. Peach greeted him, offering his left hand to shake. There were hundreds of people, all coming at different times of the day, to live in the station for a while. For some time away from harsher elsewheres. Peach had heard most of their stories, told to him as he played on the piano. This man in particular had got marooned in Newcastle after working to infiltrate the IRA back in the 80's. There had been reason to believe the city was being used as a go-between to bring in heroin to fund the army. He got sucked into an operation and never came out. Never knew what became of his daughter or wife. Never knew he could be disappeared until it happened to him. There are many places to live by the river that have peculiar locks on the doors. Peach reached inside his right breast pocket and pulled out his baccy pouch.

He gave it to the man and shook his hand again. He leaned towards Thomas and whispered,

"We've got an arrangement. Get my hat and lend him some of the change out of it. But be discreet."

Thomas bent down, he picked up the hat. As he stood up, a lady from the station - tucked uncomfortably into a tight blue dress and a bit red in the face - admonished him about putting it down to busk and that it was illegal. And, after a brief self-righteous pause, she told him his friend should play something happier. She turned and walked away back towards the platforms. Thomas blew a raspberry after her. He nudged Peach and nodded to the man wrapped in the blankets. They both stepped outside, through the glass doors beside the piano.

"The name's Michael," said the stranger.

"Thomas. Here mate, take the fiver."

"You sure? And I'll give you his baccy back."

"I think he wants you to keep it. He's quitting."

"Sure, sure." He glanced at Thomas, suspecting a joke, but in finding none he fixed his eyes on Thomas and a brief smile came to his lips. "Thanks pal."

Thomas left him rolling and looked around for the station worker as he walked inside. A couple more people stood about behind Peach. The lady was nowhere to be seen. He put the hat back down and joined Peach, resting on the glass again; searching the room for a security camera to grin at just in case.

"And what if you have to ask someone else for help explaining how to use the device or choose the biscuits?" Continued Thomas.

Peach paused, letting the last notes resound until they had filled the room and into the crevice corners. He exhaled a long, slow breathe before standing up. He gestured to Thomas to stand with him beside the piano. Another young man sat down and began playing. Peach stuck his hands into his pockets and turned to his friend.

"Do you know what you're asking for or how to ask for it?" Asked Peach. "If you make a mess in asking, then you get something completely different, who is at fault? You or the provider? Let's stick with communication as an example. That to want and need are two severely different desires; that wanting and the desire to want have been engineered to make the desirous perceive them as a need. That we need to communicate with others is a pure desire, perhaps native human behaviour, but that we desire to do so through email or phone is what we have learnt to do and I believe is maladaptive and has observable, negative, impacts on human health and sense of self. That is control."

"And people force each other to use these forms of communication because it's 'what everyone is doing' right?" Asked Thomas.

"Yes," replied Peach, "and thus you come around to a situation with a giant amount of people doing something that they have not chosen for themselves as the popular means of communication. They have had to adapt to it, endure its consequences; having virtual social networks with quantifiable measures instead of communities. But apart from choosing what device to use, they have receded from the idea that there could be something else instead. A different way to communicate."

"And whether people really want to see what that alternative is, I don't know."

"Well science fiction is still popular," quipped Peach, "so I reckon they do, in a way, but living it vicariously and living it are two different states of being."

"It's also hard to step away from phones and emails because other people rely on you to participate."

"Yep," sighed Peach. "It also requires us to know how to regulate our use of them, or to adapt to trusting each other in a new way; again."

"Or that, but the addictive force of flashing lights is really enticing and in some places it's more colour than you see in the streets for months! I mean look at this island we live on."

"It's also weird, being able to get information from the internet and it has no direct relationship to the world around you. Or when you walk through a city centre and as you look around there are so many people taking photographs of themselves and each other, or busy on their phones. All under the guise of sharing."

"It's insidious, that's what it is, and disorientating," said Thomas, pursing his lips and breathing slowly out of his nose. "Sometimes, it feels like I'm watching a family of peacocks that are trapped in a drunken waltz."

"Ha, now you're becoming emotional and preachy?"

"Shut up," Thomas jabbed at Peach's arm, "I'm not preaching. The displacement of self in the world of devices, whilst living in real space is upsetting. To be in a place, anywhere, and access context-less information of a shocking event or with dramatic, emotional repercussions is a form of distraction and puts us ever in the realm of potential anxiety, but also in the realm of potential joy which is confusing for a human. Which state are you supposed to live in?

"Both?"

"Sarky bastard. I just wish it would change."

Thomas breathed out, letting his head and shoulders fall forward. He closed his eyes. It took a moment of breathing to restore him to himself. Peach squeezed his hand and stepped back towards the piano, as the young man left to catch a train.

He started a melody in B major with his right hand. He stretched out his left hand. Thomas came over and leant on the piano, watching Peach concentrating on the keys. He never told Peach how much enjoyed watching him play the piano. He kept that joy inside himself, quietly.

"I got a couple of messages last week," began Peach, coming out of a reverie as his left hand joined in with the bass line. "One told me about a couple having a baby, the other about a relative dying, one from a friend having a relationship crisis. All whilst I was painting one wall at the theatre. You know, I'm busy and empathetic, but I can't deal with being pulled in so many directions. It makes me a bit jumpy."

"You, Peach? Jumpy?"

"Yeah, it happens," he looked up at Thomas, showing his stained and crooked teeth as he grinned. "Being able to learn such information, at any moment of the hour, is fascinating, but that we can no longer control the environments or places where we receive said information is concerning, no? That every social space becomes imbued with meaning that is alien to it, it's disorientating, I think. This is also where, possibly, the integration and obsessive engagement with social media in our lives has gone too far. Fucking influencers my arse!" Peach spread both hands wide as he played a loud and haunting middle section. He rocked backwards and forwards as he played, looking like a part of the hammer mechanism inside. He returned to the calmer, earlier melody. "Maybe we lose our grounding through this attachment to social media in public spaces."

"Maybe that's also a point where we lose the desire to form communities," added Thomas, drawing his arms around himself. "What need would we have to do it, if we are part of something bigger than ourselves that is encased within this box in our hands?"

"All of this exists a weird vacuum, lacking the emotion that's so important to communication. Instead of emotion we have what, symbols that represent emotions? Fuck, it's a joke. I'd wager that lack of emotion on a communication level slowly drives people towards more excessive seeking of emotions or of some fulfilling stimulus."

"That seeking also makes it easier to hate," added Thomas. "In these online forums or comment spaces, there is no real response there for you to interact with. You see no human respond to your words or your thoughts. The unfulfilled need lends to the language of hate that can escalate. Then when someone replies with an equal if not more extreme response the volley becomes heated. As text, as a script, all they can do is become more and more vitriolic. There is no opportunity for catharsis."

"True. And if the starting point is also full of tension and angst, it's no wonder people can't just sit and be and observe the world around them when they're not on their devices. Everyone is antsy. And then, if tech products keep developing like a 1950's sci-fi novel, the advent of techno glasses or bionic eyes that could transmit these text messages or our social media onto the world around us is scary, but possible and yet more of this future of the past shite that we have to contend with."

As Peach continued playing, Thomas mimed the act of beaming his social media onto the glass wall beside the piano. His hands forming the owl eye binoculars he had learnt as a child.

"Imagine, instead of only getting updates, constant progression towards the better experience, imagine if the way we used them could adapt. Fuck, what needs to happen in our culture

190

to make it less likely for parents to give their kids these devices so early on in life? The redistribution of wealth, or the reconceiving of time could help. But do we teach the children that these technologies are ways to cope, or ways to engage with each other? What happens if they don't develop relationship soft skills?"

"Yeah, but how could you make that case?" Asked Thomas. "How could you ask so many people to reconsider? When it's as popular as it is."

"Ah mate, you want me, one person, to figure out the stress of timing and waiting for a scandal and having to plant a seed at the right time in a warp-paced information environment? The whole of today I've been talking about a part of a much bigger whole. You cannot change the whole if you don't interact with the parts. And the assumption that I, one person, is up to fixing the whole world is absurd! It requires everyone engaging with it. That's why I'm interested in the stories people share, how they relate the world to themselves and others, that's my part in all this. That's what I feel my part is, anyway. But I digress. That crazy pace of developments is, in part, why we struggle to know how to enter into the discussion in a competitive environment. We are, as the public, never really consulted in all of these advances and changes. Most of it is developed to be consumed in order to keep the economy burning like one of the furnaces in Blake's vision."

"You know," interjected Thomas, "I think we've also forgotten what questions or *problems* some of these technologies were supposed to be the answer for."

"Yes, perhaps one day we'll be able to laugh at how the means to communicate made more people lonely than at any point in human existence."

Peach and Thomas looked at each other for a moment. Peach looked over the piano and saw a small audience in the reflection behind him. A brief smile curled up at the left corner of his mouth. Playing in the station helped settle him when all his thoughts were a rioting in his imagination. He let his fingers find their ways over the keys, embellishing a descent from the high end, before crashing down on the bottom B note. He dove back up to the higher octaves into intricate cascades and little runs; his mouth open and eyes staring at the keys as his attention focused on the act of playing. He laughed as he ran through scales leading back to the bass end, each peal of laughter growing from a deeper place within him.

The melody relented and he eased out of the trance he had fallen into, but let his fingers continue playing.

"But you know mate," began Peach, his eyes still fixed on the piano, "in conversations, discussing the ways in which we use these technologies can begin at any point, or in art, or through comedy; the possibility of change grows and can be shared. And it's in conversation, in dialogue, when ideas hatch and actions are made, then reflected upon. That is also the place where, as a human, we can experience the infinite and the impossible number of options we have. Even the ones that include a step away from progress as a social mantra. Take a humane approach and go, starting as fast or as slow as suits the group you're in."

"Funny really, that the false argument of 'you're talking about moving backwards', by suggesting a slackening of the pace of technological development, or working in a closer connection with the earth, equates to a time when things were simpler in some peoples' minds."

"There has never been a simple time and what I propose is not simple either. What the fuck even is simple?" Peach cried out, raising his arms. "What about humanity has ever been simple?

Simple is a comparative delusion for means of manipulation. This life is majestic and peculiar and an intrigue! To call it simple is to rob us of the opportunity to live passionate and wonderful lives. That other options to contemporary culture are ruled out as primitive or too simple to be worth trying is maddening and hypocritical. That this one we live in relies so heavily on the augmentation of entire continents of people into ignorant stereotypes is worthy of remembrance. In the name of what? Under the auspice of 'developing forward thinking futures…' The 'forward thinking' position is untenable, it comes from a culture that revolves, relies on self-sustaining, forward is not really an option, but life can be so much more than a singular linear narrative. It also means we can consider our resources better. Are we prepared enough? Do we have access? Can we trade? Do our tradable commodities rely on industry or call centres? Do we create work or benefit schemes? Do we rely on slavery to extract the minerals in your devices? But I digress."

Peach lifted his chin toward the ceiling and pounded on the full octave notes and the middle section, again, in a way that would bring pride to dead Rachmaninov.

"You know, what's wrong with sitting down for a moment?" He shouted over the piano. "You know the old saying? 'To your sins and your arse.'"

"When it's all a bit too much you've still got your arse to sit on and reflect on what happens next. Instead of continuing to strive 'forward' but to branch out, as electricity does in all our human circuitry, in a myriad of directions."

"That's the one!" Peach broke off from the raucous noise he was making and dropped into a variation that was a bit more like a dance progression that would have suited the 80's in Manchester. Then from nowhere he stopped.

"Mate, have we got enough in the hat for a toastie at Alphabetti yet?" asked Peach, slouching forward; resting his hands on the piano for support.

Thomas went over and picked up the hat. The people listening dropped in some more coins and a few stepped forward and whispered into Peach's ears before heading into the night.

"I think there's enough," said Thomas.

Chapter 8. Stories that make us human.

A big line of traffic clogged up Neville Street, tailing back to the High-Level Bridge. Someone, in a battered and emerald green VW golf, was blaring Love Island by Fatboy Slim from bass-heavy speakers. Peach and Thomas reached the street as the beat dropped. Some rowdy lads in white shirts and rugby ties dry humped the car before running up Grainger street. The cars crawled forward. The loud scronks of a saxophone, the kick drum thud and belching distortion of a band sound checking in the basement of Head of Steam, fused with the next track from the car. A phalanx of doormen in black, all with matching shaved back and sides, headed up past Gorman's statues. A lady with a large wicker basket and floral sari held the hand of a child, waiting for the green man on the traffic lights to appear. The stained glass of the Catholic Cathedral glowed a cloudy red. The taxi drivers shouted at the other drivers for blocking lanes. Gothic teenagers emerged from the side door of the supermarket in the station. The sky deepened and the flickering street lights, headlights and the spot lights of the Dog and Parrot pub illuminated the street. A man in desert camouflage gear huddled over on the steps of the Co-Op Childcare centre. The stench of spilt beer, sugary vodka and shrill screams from Times Square poured into the junction beneath the giant 'Life' sign for the science village and research centre that surrounded the square. Plumes of shisha smoke curled up from mouths under a canopy outside Wafi Lounge. Peach pointed over to the Dog and Parrot on the corner.

"You know, that's where Alphabetti started."

Ali, the artistic director of the theatre Peach had helped rebuild, had approached the landlord at the start of 2012, during a week when the pub had been closed for cleaning. The night before there had been a heavy metal gig, where the lead singer – wearing a gimp suit - zipped the microphone to his mouth and proceeded to decimate a pig's head with a baseball bat over the audience. As the landlord sloped around with a mop, he'd asked if the pub would be interested in theatre. The landlord had jumped at it and a relationship grew. It became the first site of the theatre, born out of a need to put on work which had no other home in the city. Like many things it evolved, moved; survived.

They walked past the brickwork paintings of Bowie and Prince. A drag queen doorman smoked outside Eazy Street. The grilled kebab and fried chicken stink boiled away behind greasy rivulets mapped in the condensation on the key-scratched take away windows. The shouts for gin pitched out of the corner shops and the queers at the cash machine bickered about buying a round of poppers before Powerhouse. The rainbow colours stood high, lit up beneath the turning sky. Couples jumped the lights in front of minivans to avoid the stagger and inquiry of the tramps. The well-dressed medical students stepped into Akbars air-conditioned vestibule, unconcerned by the shrieking breaks and shouts. In the neon shadows of Waterloo street, a tight polo collared teen threw up in his takeaway box and others laughed.

On the corner of West Morland and St James Boulevard they hung about the junction, all ways thick with cars and screaming exhausts beneath the nocturnal twilight sky on a Thursday evening.

"And that's where it is now," Peach held Thomas's shoulders and turned him, a little to the right.

Across the boulevard, behind an avenue of ash trees and lit up by a handful of light bulbs was the chipboard and acrylic sign of Alphabetti Theatre.

"There's a great deal of my pride in that place."

During the June of 2017, Peach had visited Thomas. He had been worried that Thomas was slipping into despondency. He hadn't heard from him in over a month, calls unanswered, messages unseen. He appeared one Wednesday morning as Thomas was getting home from the morning shift. It had been a tough morning and the first thing Thomas heard, as he stepped onto Sidney Grove, was a voice bellowing at him that he had shit in his hair. His head had fallen forward and he had ignored the shout. Peach almost missed him before he got in the door, but tenderly grabbed his friends' elbow and pulled him back.

Peach pulled the shit from his hair and showed it to him. Thomas wept from weariness and sadness and held onto Peach as tight as his tired arms could. Peach nursed Thomas back to a calmer state of self, by listening and keeping him company at the odd free times he had. But, whilst Thomas was at work, Peach roamed the city. He went to explore the Discovery museum exhibitions and to see the Turbinia steamship. As he left the museum he saw, across the car park, a small group of people carrying a couple planks of timber and tools into a building. Peach asked what they were building and, by the end of the afternoon, was part of the group gutting an old rubber stamp factory and building a theatre in its place.

The days had been long and there was no pay. There is often a confusion of the role of volunteers, funding and where the money comes from to afford the luxury of working for free. This is a misconception and a confusion wrought from a variety of circumstances and manipulative mouths. Peach's life was in no way enviable, nor a luxury. He had, by some standards, no stability and no way of knowing what would come of helping them build; or after it. It is easy to judge what the other person has that belittles your own circumstance or confines, while ignoring the deficits and stresses of theirs. It is divisive and ruins chances at forming community, pitting self against another. It is a centuries old practice that is coming to an end.

Thomas and Peach arrived in the entryway to the theatre. Through the giant windows in front of them they saw the bar, vivid with people and luminous in comparison to the dark grey paint of the hall.

There was a full house of people in the bar. Some were seated at the handmade tables, some standing between them; some stuffed into corners and nooks. Someone cracked their head on the disco ball in the booth that occupied the broken-down lift. The coal black Staffy slumped on the chesterfield sofa next to a lady wrapped in bright colours who was concentrating on a notebook full of stage designs and pencil shavings. Reclaimed wood had been fashioned into a pair of giant book cases, packed to spilling; a pair of pensioners fondling the covers beneath the letter J. On a raised step in the alcove, beneath a small clouded window, stood a Steinway baby grand piano; donated from a friend of the theatre. A couple of women sat on the stool, watching the room; holding one another's' hands with pints of local lager in the other. A song about Walt Whitman's niece bustled about their ears and swam between the glasses on the painter's plank bar shelf, beneath a bust of Bowie.

During the last month that Peach had been staying with Thomas, he'd gotten into the habit of waking up early and walking to the theatre to play piano before sunrise. He held a key so he could come and go during the renovation work he was doing upstairs in the theatre offices. He wouldn't turn the lights on until he finished playing. The ritual settled him.

Peach had been living in Innsbruck for the best part of a year, trying to piece back together a relationship that had enthralled and opened him up, but one that he had torn apart during the year before. His appetite for the living was not suited to attempting a long distant relationship. No matter how intense it felt when they were together. Try as he might to adapt, he could not become a patient lover. The time between seeing each other was always too long. They had met, by chance, after a festival in Italy. He could not stay; she could not go. So, they tried, but he slept with someone else and hid it from her. Inevitably, she found out.

That was the wound he had been healing in Innsbruck. She had been shocked, for a change, having had her own affairs in the past and being accustomed to feeling always desired. Despite the insults and harangues that continued for a couple of weeks after she ended the relationship, the light never truly died.

Six months later, after an invitation from the mountainside festival organisers, he arrived in Italy to play piano. And she was there, right at the front of the audience. She had come with the intention of showing off her new lover to make him jealous. Only there had been no new lover. A brief romance with a woman on the island of Elba, on the black magnetic sands encircled in candles, but no more. After his set opened the festival, she clambered over the field fence to find him behind the stage. They had stared at one another for a moment before embracing and kissing.

He found a place to live just outside the Innsbruck, a quarter the way up the mountain on the southside of the valley, and they began a cleansing ritual of sorts. They argued and shouted their way across the city, raging in tears outside the Hof Garten; bawling at each other on the Maria Theresa Strasse; screaming and kissing in the glacial river Sill behind the Bergisel; falling in and out of love with each rise and fall of the moon.

Between the endless cycle of turmoil and tenderness he struggled to gather the regional dialect or enough Deutsch to get by. He couldn't find any meaningful work, other than moonlighting as a private event cook for cash in hand. Everything precarious, everything snagging on the paranoia of being indebted to other people who had learnt his language because of the sway of history. He trapped himself, wrapped up the corners of his imagination and protected himself against the fear that what was happening was only possible because of a horrific process of Colonisation. The place he was staying at fell away. The people in the house had to renovate the basement he was sleeping in because a three-inch carpet of mould they had found in the foundations. He tried living in the building site, then on a mattress by the back door with the cat, before finding a room in a weird block of flats; a leftover from the Olympics in 1976. He'd been living there with students and refugees, slowly losing his sense of self in the face of ignorance about the Austrian legal, financial, bureaucratic systems. He went silent and knew he had to step away from the city. He had made his case to her and promised it was not the end. He needed to catch his thoughts again. He arrived in Newcastle at the start of April after hitch-hiking north through Germany and France.

The two weeks that he'd been back had helped, but still the insecurity and the fraught phone calls between them often rattled him. They were trying to agree on a place to meet, in England, where they could walk. In the hope that the relationship could continue to grow. Peach and Eva, a pair by peculiar design.

—

From a door behind the bar emerged a lady. On her head was a tousled mane of black hair. She wore an old bottle blue knitted jumper, with an articulated fish ear ring in her right ear, and a harried look on her face; her eyebrows perched above the rim of her glasses, with eyes wide open. Contrary to her expression, she spoke in a calm tone, to the young man sat in the box office booth at the end of the bar; who was busy poking at the peeling posters and drifting off into his thoughts. She stepped from behind the bar, with a list of names in her hand. She stopped in front of Peach, smiled and squeezed his elbow as she nodded at him. Lauren, a local legend of comedy in the city, and all-rounder in the running of the theatre. She had found Peach agreeable and got on well with him; accepting his louder moments and quirks. She had also corralled his unruly nature at times when he lost sight of his boundaries; for that he was eternally thankful. The friendship that had grown between them was a big part of the reason he had considered changing a few of his more irksome habits. She darted inside the theatre doors that stood askew. Peach and Thomas found a bit of wall space to lean on as the congregation waited.

Two middle-aged men sat at the table beside them, deep in a chat. One, with bristled chin, broad shoulders and flat cap broke off and stood up beside Peach.

"'ere, are you alright mate? You're looking a bit thin, you know, we've been really worried about you like. Always, you know I worry about you."

His friend, with beaming blue eyes behind square frames and a shaved head, joined in; his old dockers coat falling to the floor.

"Aye, and how's that balloon?" He stooped down to pick up his coat. "Have you got that hot air balloon yet? Eh? Av' ya?"

Both of them took one of Peach's hands and started shaking it. He introduced Thomas to the pair and they greeted him with warmth and attention. They were regulars in the house and a charming duet of eager, earnest playwrights of the contemporary human comedy. Honest as fisherman, mad as Indian mathematics.

The theatre doors swung open and Lauren waded through the crowd towards the bar. From the far end she nodded at the man in the box office who paused the music. The theatre bell rang and thrummed over the swells of people as she called out the opening of the evenings show.

Peach offered to stand the pair a pint later as he pushed them towards the door. Pints were necked, people squeezed past each other, a glass shattered and the Staffy barked at the mess and melee; at the rabble of curious people.

The doors closed. Peach and Thomas stood at the bar and ordered a house cheese toastie and a pair of ginger beers from Lauren. She stepped into the back room. Peach turned to Thomas.

"Consider the popular 'story arc'. Linear, beginning, conflict, resolution. Nothing in our experience of life is so simple, it gives false hope."

His hand stuck to the spilt ale on the bar and he wiped it off on his coat.

"And after enough repetition the spectacle and allure has worn off," Thomas added.

"Revolutions have been televised and they have a pretty music score to accompany them. Metaphors only suit the tongues that are refined enough to taste them, not like salt; goes good on everything. Not enough aspects of life are taken into account and to accept that natural progression refuses to engage with the influence and position of other characters is daft. It is not in the story, the narrative, therefore it is not plausible, no longer conceivable. What would happen though, if in order to get our culture and its participants on the same page, we created children's stories that work on a circular motion or that lead to metamorphosis. Before the beginning is the end and we travel through the story to reach that point again. And by the time you reach the end again you can make a step beyond. Progression is possible." He paused and swigged from the bottle of ginger beer. "That's why I liked Bacon Knees."

"Bacon what?" asked Thomas.

"Bacon Knees and Sausage Fingers, by Steve Byron and Gary Kitching. It's a play that loops through and through itself allowing the intense and peculiar pasts of these two odd characters, that meet on the High-Level bridge, to catch up with them and then travel beyond the point of their meeting. This style of narrative is also there in the great story telling comedy of Billy Connolly and Dylan Moran. Their long tangents that begin with the punchline, or an eruption of laughter, and then go back to work up to the start, leaving you feeling more human afterwards because you're laughing with him, not at him. By comparison, the rise in self-deprecating or out-right aggressive comedy relies on a sense of pity or nervous tension to get laughter, but Moran's and Connolly's are stories that make us human."

"Perhaps," mused Thomas, "it isn't the story style that needs redefining. If we return to a status quo as it were, perhaps it's the existing conditions that are in need of changing? If our state of affairs – I mean what we encounter when we walk out of the performance, venue, storytelling – were more interactive somehow, if the world we lived in took into account all of the stories we have learnt from."

A chorus of muffled laughs squirmed through the cracks in the soundproofing. It wasn't tight, by any stretch of the imagination, but considering the dense mess of pipes and the lack of a straight line in the wall frame, Peach had done the best he could. Often, he had hung onto the old gas pipes and struts that supported the electrical cables, sucking in the fibreglass from the insulation as he hammered it into place with his palms or cut strips off the sides to make it fit. To complete the internal section, he worked between the walls, wedged inside; standing on nothing as he drilled and cut and fit the material into place.

"Yes, I wonder if you could encourage everyone within the culture to accept that. That's what I mean, if you could really interact, form a tangible relationship with the world around you in some way. Where you can see the impact that what you have learnt can have on your environment. Instead of falling again into this conglomeration of franchised shite. Then, perhaps, we would feel our own ability to step away from the linear view of progressive culture that repeats itself in so many ways. This is why building walls of communities is better than just standing and being photographed. That kind of interactive, not virtual reality interactive experiences."

Peach looked up at the wall behind the box office. He told Thomas about the time he dropped the drill. It only happened once. He hung upside down between the cavity wall and the bar wall, fingers outstretched and his hips were stuck between the frames, swearing and laughing; until he grasped it and hoisted himself upright.

Lauren returned from the back room with two plates. Peach's already had a dollop of brown sauce on it. She had, for years, been a rover of the island and knew the importance of simple gestures. As Peach had gotten to know her, it seemed she had a hand in everything to keep the theatre running. Including sending Ali home when he forgot to leave.

"Imagine, having the capacity to change that thought pattern, preparing for the next 'revolutionary force', but instead of going around again, or further along the line, we jumped off? By the point in the cycle, when a culture shows a need to change, it is usually under a great period of stress and exhaustion: does it not fit that a deeper need for a period of rest and cooperation, for a care-giver is necessary, not another upheaval, not more impoverished life, not more political dick waving between America and North Korea – with billions of lives spread about in between. Instead of finding a new scapegoat, continuing to point fingers, why can't we take a moment to rest and reflect or, like the stroppy seven-year-old boy at the party who is tired, but hasn't yet developed the conscious ability to take himself to sleep, stop struggling and be taken to bed?

"You and this seven-year-old mate, how many times?"

"But it's true! So many aspects of our culture point towards this need for a rest, to the point where the message has been buried beneath metaphor. Imagine if, turning the attentiveness

212

of insecure masculinity into a carer and watching the role of mediator and creator being fulfilled by the feminine."

Thomas coughed up part of his toastie at the sound of care work.

"But, why is it so clear cut as masculine and feminine, eh mate?" Asked Thomas. "What if these parts of us were deeper and simpler than the obscurity of masculine and feminine?"

Peach nodded in consent. He carried on eating, the sauce sticking to the corner of his lips. Doors opened and closed behind them. The bulbs hummed about and a taxi gunned its engine on the boulevard, racing against a motorbike.

"It's also in modern folk music, all this screaming out for emotional stability for at least a decade now, with its reverb heavy drums beating like a call to *look at me*, but by the time you look everyone's dancing the slow step or the desolation or, as happens at so many concerts now, no one's dancing at all."

"It's almost as if the words don't mean anything."

"Perhaps, but do we still struggle with this repetition because there are so few spaces to move into with these new feelings, these new desires? I think all of the ideas are already there, they're rising above and bouncing just beneath the surface. That's why I'm hopeful, I think we're so close to this metamorphosis. The intervention of the care-giver is necessary to put that child to sleep, in the same way a period or generation of care is necessary to settle and put to rest the nightmare of this civil project on this island, and from it we could learn the lessons of how to heal from this isolation we've developed from each other, from the world at large and from life. All of it, the conspiracy theorists, the elite group, the 'other', the exotic misanthropy of Utopia and Dystopia, the glaring lights of spectacle, the undressing of a woman on a screen across the whole planet in private and public, is it not there to be seen that this greed-lust is the consequence of a male dominated culture run on the logic of a stroppy seven-year-old? We can do so much better.

"I can't agree with all this academic and philosophical nonsense, that all people perceive reality as a fiction to comprehend it. What rubbish, a surface level observation, the deep rut of human inertia in our culture is cynicism and apathy towards a culture that has created only its own necessity rather than much of anything useful; other than resignation to a belief that our situation cannot and will not change. This is a consequence of culture on an infinite loop. Revolution! *Shibanyatsi!* Talk to anyone in this city, irrespective of background, socio-economic status, education levels; they each have their own way of saying the same thing."

"They all acknowledge the present is shit, that they have to work too much and that it's not their fault," added Thomas.

"Fine, and a generation ago someone once wrote that there is nothing to be done, but there is always something that can be done about it. Resignation is only the beginning of something new, the modern definition implies a separation from something no longer desirable. In our culture, that separation was once the 'road' novel or the grand ventures into the world, or simply to your cousins in Scarborough, but at present even that separation has been subsumed back into the rhetoric of this culture. Young colonials head out into the world to seek the ever-expanded white man's paradise, with his 'ever-plastic excuse' as Roy Harper once phrased it. That 'plastic excuse', currency, the credit card and the modern fascination with debt or being indebted to someone else, I believe is a result of decades or centuries of accepting a position of gratitude instead of one of appreciation. To be grateful is to be subservient to that which has caused awe or inspiration or provided for us, it's being bailed out, whilst carrying on in much the same way. But what if all this didn't need separation? What if we could rotate and express this need in a different way?"

Peach reached into his pockets and pulled out a grubby handkerchief. He rubbed his fingers clean and ordered another ginger beer.

"To appreciate is to consider ourself equal in some way to that which has stirred our wonder, our respective gravities are different, but that *we are worthy*. Not only that we are worthy, but we are equal because we are a part of it. Equality is not logical or possible based on a competitive culture where there must be a hierarchy, a victor and losers; equality is a false argument, a moons-noon-light in our culture, it is absurd."

"It's Orwell and the pigs" added Thomas.

"Gratitude is a supplicant at the altar, appreciation is a cause for reflection which can lead to a reasoned decision to alter one's actions or behaviour. I appreciate the fact that our culture has created some brilliant forms of communication and that human endeavour has been enabled by funding invested from this mad economy, but I think it needs to change. I struggled for many years with this idea, too young and seduced by the grand Napoleonic tirades I used to drink through, but it was my sister who would always remind me, there are some people who will not listen to a loud and shouty bastard. Thus, I believe, that it needs to begin with a change of perspective, not so much needs to change physically, no seizing through force, no existential despair of staring into mirrors watching women grow beards, just a small change of perspective. It's the scrabble example. What's the point in creating a new game, more stuff? That requires more waste, more outsourced ill-paid labour that has a massive impact on the environment, not to mention the amount of capital one would need to fund and market a new game. The desire to create something new, to be heralded as the novel saviour is bollocks. In a time, such as this, it makes more sense to take what we have, stop trying to brand it with our personality and self-seeking desire and use what is already in front of us, but in a different order. Scrabble exists, it doesn't need marketing as it already has its own appeal and reputation. Besides, being skint as I invariably am, one has to resort to what is available and work with it. To at least start now."

Thomas sucked his fingers clean of cheese grease. He excused himself from Peach and went to the toilet. When he came back Peach was sat on the sofa. Both hands busied with massaging the shoulders of the Staffy.

"I was once told that 'appreciate' is a word most people don't know, let alone know how to spell. I used to get told a lot that my words were too big, but is it really? Is it worth considering the pettiness of a man who in order to heal himself has begun to rewrite the myth of Sisyphus?"

"Is that what you did?" Asked Thomas, as he sat next to Peach and the dog.

"No, someone I met. He was willingly undertaking a task which has no logical end to heal himself. Is that not absurd? He will never be healed. A man forever pushing a rock up a hill. Is that not a paradox? That one seeks to be healed through continuously engaging in only the act of healing? That the conclusion, of being healed, is not what he is working towards, but rather the prolonged wait. Is that not also a symptom of this culture, in some form of sadomasochism, we want to remain on this road to salvation, to being healed, rather than facing up to what being healed would actually mean and feel like? Is that not absurd?"

"Yes, Peach. It is. And we're surrounded by posters, billboards; advertising the need to heal and correct our habits. And yet, the people who profit from our habits do not listen to themselves. They act as if they're outside of our world, as if they were masters of a universe. Busy playing kings, instead of living with people."

"Yes mate! Everywhere there are voices and advertisements for being healed, in ever more exhausted and incapable ways to be saved, but they never reach an end point even if you buy into the rhetoric. That we know we need to be healed, but there is still an anxiety and suspicion towards what that state would be, to being in effect content. To be in a state of satisfaction and to fall off the precipice of the universe as we know it onto a carpet only three feet below and carry on walking. The same in many ways, only a little different. The madness of knowing what we need and of being so close to it. It's in the essence of the desire to travel, to move."

"Perhaps movement is a native human trait," Thomas leant back on the sofa and rolled his head from shoulder to shoulder.

He gazed around the bar, imagining Peach stuck in between the walls. Another muffled laughter came from within the theatre. They both sat silent for a moment, digesting the room.

Thomas turned to Peach, resting a hand on his arm.

"Do you want to carry on walking?" Asked Thomas.

Peach considered. "Could do. I just need to pay. Can I invite you to your drink and toastie on your first day being unemployed?"

Thomas's eyes widened then his whole face seemed to relax.

"You can. I'd forgotten about that." He pushed Peach towards the bar with a playful shove and got off the sofa himself. Peach settled up with Lauren and left enough for a round in the taps for the other two.

They walked towards St James' stadium beneath the glowing streetlights that obscured the night sky. Taxi's jumped the junction lights, a drunk rubbed his fingers on the windows of the chippy by the West road bus stop. Shouts flew out of windows like belched verses. The stadium, faced by the glass and illegally clad high-rise blocks, was open. People were hanging around the bar, drinking expensive lager, betting on foreign football and smoking. In the bowels of the stadium was the end of the Metro line.

"Do you want to go up through Leazes park?"

"Yes lets," answered Peach.

They passed through the car park and climbed the steps beside the station entrance. The lights of the Strawberry pub were on and laughter echoed within.

They turned left on Leazes Park road and saw the regulars in front of Bar Loco. A couple live-in vans were parked outside. A group of people were busy hauling a sound system inside. Dogs wandered through peoples' legs. The suits and the trackies side by side. Shouts and snorts of laughter behind pint glasses erupted inside and out. The plumes of smoke, unfurling from parted lips; escaping into the evening sky.

"It is odd to deny that need to move on," began Peach.

"But it isn't just a denial of it mate," interrupted Thomas. "Some people just don't have the means to move on. Look at me. I can't leave the house I live in for example. But that's why looking at things differently helps to begin with. If we move to a new perspective of what we have around us, if we engage with it in a slightly different way, perhaps we can 'move on'."

They crossed through another car park and between a gap in the terrace. The light over their heads shivered. They paused at the entrance to the park. A couple of people were still throwing a basketball around on the courts below. They were watched by a group of silhouettes, huddled beside the fences, clouded in smoke. The smell of piss damp grass and doner meat. Peach took up Thomas's hand and turned to face him.

"True. Sometimes I think about how close we are to what we need. It has to be seen as a bit of a dark comedy especially when so many people are able to move around and yet spend time ticking boxes, lists, satisfying the ego driven personalities they have adopted from a designed and prescribed way of living. The Westerners who arrive at Ashrams in India, adorn the dress of the Kundalini apprentice – a costume seldom worn by locals – and superficially absorb the lessons of the yogi, to then return to their homes full of cultural appropriation and self-righteousness and force it upon others, but then years later stand bickering over plastic tubs when the charm has worn off and they are no longer unique. It is flawed is it not? To find what it is that we need to show others, but not accept it in ourselves long enough to change our actions and engage with others in a sincere way."

"I think," Thomas squeezed Peach's hand in return, "it's also about having the place to practice and support the ideas we have learnt. We can't be separate or stuck in insular communities forever. Gets us nowhere."

"Nowhere," he echoed.

Peach put his lips together and stretched them thin by clenching his cheeks. It was an odd face, a bit like a trumpeter pursing air for the crescendo. The light faltered and they found themselves in darkness. Thomas heard Peach chuckle.

"Pfwer, pfwer, puh, puh," he carried on, dipping his shoulders from side to side.

"Fuck are you doing?"

223

"New dark park? What? Polar Bear? Come on, it's a great track."

They heard a bottle crash into the tarmac footpath. The light spat back into life. Peach, incredulous at Thomas's not knowing the English jazz band, took him by the forearm and they stepped into the park as he continued; pretending to be a saxophone as they went.

Chapter 9.   The First Juniper Tree. Newcastle by night.

The gaunt face of the Royal Victoria Infirmary loomed up on the other side of Richardson road; its windows peering over the railings into the park. The lights of an arriving ambulance danced off the pitch black of the lake. The geese huddled under the benches; the path littered with shit. A couple of fishermen smoked inside their dome tents beside the water, red ends tending their lines that illuminated like tendrils of light reaching to the sky every time a car cast its light on the junction coming out of the short stay car park.

Peach and Thomas turned left and stepped onto the grass beside the path towards the band stand.

"I mean, if we want to get deep and connected about this, when you look closely at plant biology and the cellular structure of the entire planet," Peach gestured at the horse-chestnut and the sycamores, "it all functions on cooperation, or collaboration if you want a less loaded term. People recognised this idea centuries ago and they weren't esoteric wild-hearts and the idea before them was there in different words. The formation of the universe is the result of matter cooperating with each other to form something more than the sum of itself;

the cooperation between electricity, blood, tissue, fibre, fluid, flesh and feet mixed with the same degree of curiosity that took Mohammed to the mountain, and as it says: 'Mohammed went to the mountain; the mountain was there'.

"The simplicity of it, to arrive. That which you sought is knowable and can be appreciated in it's being there and that is satisfaction enough; it does not need to be objectified or reduced to science or consumer culture. That which we seek, unity and understanding and acceptance of the intelligent chaos of this universe, is achievable. For me it is also evidence that the idea of mature gratification is a pleasurable and invaluable asset to human development and to our stories. Sometimes, to be in awe of the mystery is enough. Instead of using language to reduce the experience of Mohammed beside the mountain or, taking a plane or a car to the mountain to observe it, or the struggle for some to comprehend its' simplicity. The effort put in to *understanding it all* makes living arduous for some; drives some of them mad."

They both sat on a bench beside the bandstand. The ribs of the stadium's roof stuck out above the office windows, reaching into the evening sky. When Thomas used to sit in the park – on the evenings he couldn't face going home or into public or anywhere else in the city -, he wondered what it would be like to stand up there and see the city. He would count and un-count the ribs, imaging flags of silken fabric lapping up the wind between them. He thought about the people he would never know who came to watch the matches. He dreamt of the sounds of 40,000 people roaring together with the weight of a shared pride.

"For example, I have a desire, now, to one day see a Juniper tree," said Peach "I have only ever seen pictures. My life and actions are all geared towards one day satisfying this desire, but that I am content to gratify it at some further-off point is something I had to learn. To be patient because one day I will experience the first juniper tree in my life and, if I am ready, I will be satisfied. It will be enough. I will have arrived." He stared straight ahead, looking into the bushes around the edge of the park; the shadows moving slowly because of a light breeze.

"Is it possible that there isn't really much that a human being wants?" Asked Peach. "If so, what could happen if we stepped beyond the 'wanting' phase of human consciousness and focused all that energy somewhere else? Could be interesting, no? That's what gives me undying hope. I know life is a marvellous thing, but I don't necessarily need to know the scientific minutia of what makes it so."

Peach picked up a stone and threw it at the roof of the bandstand.

"What, too, happens if we accept the need for one another? That as a species we function, primarily, as a pack rather than as individuals? The human is more akin with the deer than with the tiger; we are graceful, powerful creatures; intuitive, but still prey. Sometimes even to monsters of our own creation. We are not enraged, slothful beasts who strike out in violent, momentous events that require so much sleep to produce the energy for such eruptions of force. We are fearful, curious and protective creatures, we are first unstable on our feet, but at full stature we are instances of pure beauty. That we have free will is debatable, yes, but that we have potential for so much more than we currently know is certain. We are capable of more than this rote mechanistic, emotional drudgery."

A trio of mallard's flew over the bandstand, heading toward the lake. A fox pushed its head through a bush, inspecting the park before it disappeared again. There was the sound of muffled, distant laughter. The gate to the adjacent moor slammed shut.

228

An engine revved on Barracks Road followed by a blast of horns.

"I believe this and it is that hope that helps me fend off cynicism and apathy and steels me against the dull repetition of revolution and violence and misanthropy and instant gratification and consumerism and the senseless, unreasonable lack of empathy that you experienced in the care role, and the other multitude of mosaic pieces that make up present life in this culture, on a small island on the edge of the Atlantic, that has caused so much strife and misery and wonder in the history of humankind; where it also rains a lot. And in that, the rain. I believe there are only two creative acts on this planet of ours that are truly worthy of recognition, the rain and pregnant women. It is the rain, the rain is the base ingredient of all sustenance on this planet, it makes the field fertile. And the pregnancy of a woman prolongs the existence of the species. All art, all media, all culture, all else is a game we have created whilst we were waiting for something else to happen, none of this is necessary, but it has been transformed into a reign of self-fulfilling logic that fashion and cosmopolitan thought supports instead of allowing for what could become of us, to allow for everyone to see the circle so that we could turn it on its side, see the tense spring and all of us let go and move onto something else."

Thomas gazed at his hands as Peach dropped into a silence. Shoulder to shoulder they remained. Peach closed his eyes and breathed deeper, down into his diaphragm; letting the air pool in the pit of his stomach before filling his lungs and slowly pushing it back into the night sky. Thomas heard the whispers of Peach's change in speed, like pistons cooling. He joined in, breathing deep, but kept his eyes on the trees; pulsing in the breeze. He felt the air wash over his exposed neck and down the collar of his shirt. He tensed his shoulders and felt the shifting ache in his lower back, sensing it as it slid from rib to rib like spilt water. Soon, he thought, the ache would subside. The days to come, that would provide the distance he needed from the abusive staff, had begun. He knew it would be slow, that the time it takes for the memories to leave the surface is immeasurable, but sure to pass; as sure as there are unknowable aspects of the universe that once will continue to hide from scientific endeavour. As Thomas looked at the leaves shimmering under the street light, he resolved to be patient with himself. Perhaps he would try to see Mary again, if only for a cup of tea at Quilliams.

Peach, shifted on the bench; pulling Thomas from his meditations.

"You know, how different life would be if we could go back to the instant when man, as in the Male, first realised he was not a creative force on this planet. When he realised, he could not produce life because he had no womb. And tell him just to sit down for minute, breathe, you are ok and just do something useful while the babies on the way. Instead of creating all this that has survived him."

Thomas leant back, cupping his hands behind his head to look for the moon; visible above the evening glow of the city.

"Peach, then what becomes of it all? Are you devaluing all of human development?"

"No. Just saying it helps me find a humour in the darkness," he sucked his cheeks in between his teeth and started to chew, "makes me feel optimistic that, in spite of all this human development, we will not force our species into extinction or some worse nightmare. That we can still play a different game." The lack of nicotine turned his stomach and his gums ached. He stood up and offered his hand to Thomas.

They walked up the pavilion steps between statues – lions missing noses; eagles without wings. A man lay on a bench beneath a blanket, facing the stars. They left the park, lingering for a moment by the gate before they walked downhill towards the main road.

"If we can argue for and work towards a small change in perspective, every-*thing* will be the same, only a little different, but that difference, though little, will create enormous potential for the species. We could live for something more than profit, what a bastard of a word. You know, how many of us are stressed because we're exhausted? How many of us make arses of ourselves or are shitty with others because we're tired and don't have what we need? When we fight and argue none of us are right, but we're all poor. And if nothing else we've got that in common."

"True enough. It's such an odd word. Profit. Prophet," said Thomas, rolling the words in his mouth.

"Mate, and what if we worked not for someone else's profit, but for each other's wellbeing. That this project of care could extend over four hundred years into the future is possible. And the desired consequence would be to create a care-providing, collaborative culture where there would be ample space for future generations to concoct new forms of culture or governance or politic. It is possible, it's all possible. All doable. And what can make it easier to move towards this is having a sense of reflection and good humour towards the paradox of a culture we live in now. It's like finding the humour in the fine maxim of Thomas Ferens."

"Who?"

"Ferens was a philanthropist of the old school, worked hard, sober and helped to fund the city of Hull. Ingenious really, a man who built an industry out of manufacturing and selling cleaning products with Lapis Lazuli to create Hull blue. I think that's what they called it. If you can see the humour in his maxim, then you can see how subtle a shift in perspective that we need to reframe our culture into one of collaboration. Remember, he was a man who sold cleaning products:

In any position you occupy, make yourself indispensable'.

Peach breathed in and out. He sniggered and looped his arm through Thomas'.

They turned right on Barracks road. The rough brickwork of Queens Court stood tall above them. Peach stopped.

"What is it mate? Thinking about going back to the piano?"

"Yes, no, maybe. No, I once saw a young Syrian girl, with hazelnut cheeks and opal eyes, on the grass in front of this building. She tied the fallen leaves of the Rowan tree back onto the low branches with soft lace, in an incorrigible labour made with the conviction of childhood. Then she was called away, back into the flats."

Thomas watched Peach's eyes close. He was elsewhere. The evening buses ferried the worrisome and weary up the hill.

"Disillusionment is the consequence of false hope. Hope is the consequence of need. Soon, I hope, she will learn she doesn't need to tie them back on."

"I hope so, for her mate," Thomas agreed.

"Imagine if, no, what's the word. Perhaps, if we could. No," Peach heaved a sigh, deflating inch by inch, "I need to play the piano mate." Peach hugged Thomas, holding him as close as he could between the lapels of his coat, "In a bit, mate."

He turned around, beginning the walk back down the hill to the station. A phone rang in his pocket. He pulled it out and answered in Deutsch.

"Für alles was war und komme, was wolle meine Liebe."

"For what was and come what may, my love," whispered Thomas, to himself, as he turned up the hill and walked toward Fenham; pulling his jacket closer before he stuffed his hands in his pockets.

Peach began discussing plans with Eva, the telephone had mediated a lot of their relationship of late, but it was agreed that at the start of the next week she would arrive in Manchester. They would head into the folds and myths of the Lake District, with a tent and the shared desire to create a life together. They knew it was possible, but hadn't quite found the right way; yet.

At the feet of St James's, people waited for their buses; buoyed by the thoughts of their journey's home. Lines of weary eyes and tired lungs. Young students sprinted across the junction – drunk, leery and shouting at the taxi drivers. The road curved in towards the heart of Grainger Town. Beneath the Chinese gate the sounds of Gaelic music bellowed out of the Irish centre. Quiet gangs of lads, with small black bags, strode past Rosie's pub - with its talking heads above the bar -, to the hum and hustle of the pool tables at Spot White.

A pair of young teachers kissed outside International house, laden with bags of paperwork across their shoulders and linguistics on their lips. The dull roar of The Gate, with its 90's house nights, cheap vodka chasers, sweat stained glass and fried chicken; the perfumes of respite. Monument, awash with thousands of people pulling this way and that for the attention of their friends' and partners, their cousins, their colleagues – wed to the uncertainty of where and how and with who, but full of the desire to be; to feel something else than the sore feet and tinnitus. All of them dancing like a mass choir of whirling dervishes that poured across the city. Spinning wildly, caught up in the catharsis of ecstasy; of their own way to express their stress. In every street, people spilled over with the lore of the night and wit as strong as a Northern wind; ambling down the cobbled Highbridge, flirting like poetry beneath the street lights, revelling to the shout and rhythm of the Baghdaddies spirited horn section and vigorous drums escaping from the fire door of Hoochie Coochie; as they stole drinks or a lighter or someone else's coat and made a run for it. Everywhere, filled with the resounding boom of raised chants and cries as powerful as the swells of the North Sea. Voices hung in the air, just below the gulls that caterwauled in return and clattered about in the debris left down the Bigg Market. In the Quayside, the raucous and the kind were side by side. In the melee there was a lady, finished the day shift as a sexual enabler for differently abled people, walking about; dragging a wagon and handing out self-made sandwiches to the homeless. Across the street people fell about, carrying one another as if the earth spun like a giant tilt-a-whirl. Alongside the Tyne, teenagers and try-hards clamoured over the railings to make an impression on their dates. And on the corner, up on the hill; in the garden of the Free Trade, a pair of friends sat down. They took their first sips of the evening and began mulling over the day like a pair of monks. They looked up and saw the great flowing Tyne before them, the bridges lacing the banks together and the city on its' Northern shore; full of light and pulsing life, vibrant and eternal – woven into the dreams of the humans living there, sewn into the skin and teeth of a passionate, honest and tender people – and they began singing:

237

" *To each new day we take new steps,*
Some big, some small,
But none shall we forget.
And as each day ends,
find a new way home
with eager, tired steps.
Some big, some small,
But none shall we forget."